MACMILLAN R
ELEMENTARY

SIR ARTHUR CONAN DOYLE

The Hound of the Baskervilles

Retold by Stephen Colbourn

MACMILLAN

ELEMENTARY LEVEL

Founding Editor: John Milne

The Macmillan Readers provide a choice of enjoyable reading materials for learners of English. The series is published at six levels – Starter, Beginner, Elementary, Pre-intermediate, Intermediate and Upper.

Level control
Information, structure and vocabulary are controlled to suit the students' ability at each level.

The number of words at each level:

Starter	about 300 basic words
Beginner	about 600 basic words
Elementary	about 1100 basic words
Pre-intermediate	about 1400 basic words
Intermediate	about 1600 basic words
Upper	about 2200 basic words

Vocabulary
Some difficult words and phrases in this book are important for understanding the story. Some of these words are explained in the story and some are shown in the pictures. From Pre-intermediate level upwards, words are marked with a number like this: …[3]. These words are explained in the Glossary at the end of the book.

Contents

A Note about This Story

This story was written by Sir Arthur Conan Doyle. It is an adventure about a detective called Sherlock Holmes. A friend of Sherlock Holmes, Dr Watson, tells the story.

Sherlock Holmes is not a policeman. He is a private detective. People pay him to find things that are lost or stolen. Holmes also solves mysteries and catches criminals.

This story takes place in 1889. There were no telephones at this time. If someone wanted to send an important message quickly, they sent a telegram.

The Hound of the Baskervilles takes place in the southwest of England on Dartmoor. Dartmoor is a wild and lonely place. Not many people live there. Dartmoor can be a dangerous place to live too.

On Dartmoor there are many high, rocky hills. These hills are called tors. There are also pieces of land called mires. These are areas of soft, very deep mud with grass growing on top. Men and animals who fall into the mires can die.

The People in This Story

Sherlock Holmes is a very clever detective. He lives and works in London at 221B Baker Street.

Dr Watson is Sherlock Holmes' friend. He helps Sherlock Holmes to solve mysteries.

Dr Mortimer lives near Dartmoor in the south-west of England. He is a doctor of medicine.

Sir Hugo Baskerville was the owner of Baskerville Hall in 1645.

Sir Charles Baskerville was the owner of Baskerville Hall at the beginning of this story. Dr Mortimer thinks Sir Charles was murdered.

Sir Henry Baskerville is the new owner of Baskerville Hall. He has come from Canada to live in England.

Mr and Mrs Barrymore are servants at Baskerville Hall.

Mr Jack Stapleton lives in Merripit House near Grimpen Mire. Stapleton is interested in the plants, birds and insects on Dartmoor.

Miss Stapleton is Jack Stapleton's sister. She lives in Merripit House. She is a tall, beautiful woman with dark hair and dark eyes.

Mr Frankland lives in Lafter Hall near Coombe Tracey. He is interested in studying the stars and has a large telescope.

Selden is an escaped prisoner from Dartmoor Prison.

1

Mr Sherlock Holmes

My name is Doctor Watson. I am writing this story about my friend, Mr Sherlock Holmes, the famous detective.

Sherlock Holmes lives at 221B Baker Street, in the middle of London. My story begins in Baker Street, one morning in 1889, when a man knocked on the door.

I heard the man say, 'Mr Holmes? My name is Dr Mortimer. I need your help.'

'Come in,' said Holmes. 'How can I help you?'

'I have a strange story to tell you, Mr Holmes,' said Dr Mortimer. 'My story is very strange. Perhaps you will not believe me.'

2

The Curse of the Baskervilles

Dr Mortimer sat down. Sherlock Holmes and I listened to his story.

'I am a doctor and I work in the country,' said Dr Mortimer. 'I live and work on Dartmoor. And, as you know, Dartmoor is a large, wild place. There is only one big house on Dartmoor – Baskerville Hall. The owner of the house was Sir Charles Baskerville. I was his friend as well as his doctor.'

'I read of his death in *The Times* newspaper,' said Holmes.

'That was three months ago,' said Dr Mortimer. 'The newspaper reported his death, but it did not report all the facts.'

'Was there something strange about his death?' asked Sherlock Holmes.

'I am not certain,' said Dr Mortimer. 'There was a story about a curse on the Baskerville family. Sir Charles believed this old story.'

'A curse?' I asked. 'What do you mean?'

'Here is the story,' said Dr Mortimer. He took a large piece of paper out of his pocket. 'Please read this. It is the story of the Curse of the Baskervilles.'

Holmes took the paper and read it. 'It is called *The Hound of the Baskervilles*,' he said. He showed me the paper. This is what it said:

In the year 1645, Sir Hugo Baskerville was the owner of Baskerville Hall. Sir Hugo was a cruel man who did not believe in God. Every day he went out hunting and drinking with a gang of wild friends.

A farmer on Dartmoor had a beautiful daughter. Sir Hugo wanted to marry the girl, but she was afraid of him. The girl's father told Sir Hugo to stay away from his farm. Sir Hugo was very angry.

One day, when the farmer was working in his fields, Sir Hugo rode to the farm with his friends. They caught the girl and took her to Baskerville Hall.

The poor girl was terrified. Sir Hugo locked her in a bedroom. Then he started drinking with his gang. When he was drunk, he became more wild and cruel. He shouted at his men and hit them.

The frightened girl waited until it was dark. Then she opened a window and escaped from Baskerville Hall.

'Please read this. It is the story of the Curse of the
Baskervilles.'

Her father's farm was about four miles away. It was night, but she was able to follow the path in the moonlight. She started to run across the dark moor.

Sir Hugo went to the girl's room. It was empty and Sir Hugo was terribly angry. He ran to his men and jumped onto the table where they were drinking. He kicked the plates and glasses off the table. 'Fetch the horses!' he shouted. 'Get the girl!'

They all ran outside and jumped onto their horses. Sir Hugo kept a pack of wild dogs for hunting. 'Let the dogs find her!' he shouted. 'The Devil can take me if I do not catch her!'

The dogs ran out across the dark moor. Sir Hugo and his men rode after them. The dogs barked and Sir Hugo shouted.

Then they heard another noise. It was louder than the noise of barking and shouting. The dogs stopped and listened. They were afraid.

The men heard the noise too. It was a loud and deep howling sound – the sound of a huge dog howling at the moon. The men stopped their horses, but Sir Hugo rode on. He wanted to catch the girl.

Sir Hugo did not catch the girl. Suddenly his horse stopped and threw him to the ground. The horse ran away in terror.

In the moonlight, the men saw a strange, black animal. It looked liked a dog with huge, fiery eyes. But it was as big as a horse. All the men became very frightened.

The huge black dog jumped on Sir Hugo Baskerville and killed him. The other men ran away into the night and Sir Hugo was never seen again.

Since that time, many of the sons of the Baskerville family have died while they were young. Many of them have died strangely. This is the Curse of the Baskervilles. The black dog – The Hound of the Baskervilles – still walks on the moor at night.

'Well, Mr Holmes, what do you think of this story?' asked Dr Mortimer.

'I do not think it is a true story,' said Sherlock Holmes. 'Why do you show me this story? Do you believe it?'

'Before Sir Charles Baskerville's death, I did not believe the story,' Dr Mortimer answered. 'But Sir Charles believed the story. It worried him. He became ill and his heart was weak.'

'Why did he believe this story?' I asked.

'Because he saw the hound on the moor,' answered Dr Mortimer. 'Or, he thought he saw it. When Sir Charles told me this story, I told him to take a holiday. I told him to go to London for a few weeks and forget all about the curse.'

'Did he take a holiday?' I asked.

'No,' said Dr Mortimer. 'He planned to go to London the following Friday. But, on the Thursday evening, he went for a walk on the edge of the moor. And he never returned.'

'How did he die?' I asked.

'He died of a heart attack,' answered Dr Mortimer. 'His servant came to fetch me. I found Sir Charles near the house, on the edge of the moor. He was running away from something when he died. I am sure of that. I think he was terrified of something.'

'Terrified?' asked Holmes. 'What was he running away from?'

'I looked at the ground where Sir Charles had walked. I saw his footprints,' said Dr Mortimer. 'But there were other footprints on the ground. They were not the footprints of a man. They were the footprints of a gigantic hound!'

3

The Problem

Holmes and I were surprised. This was a very strange story. I did not believe that Sir Charles Baskerville had been killed by a gigantic black dog. But I wanted to know the truth.

'Who else saw these footprints?' asked Sherlock Holmes. His bright eyes shone and he leant forward in his chair.

'No one else saw the footprints,' answered Dr Mortimer. 'There was a lot of rain in the night. By morning, the footprints had been washed away.'

'How large were the footprints? Were they larger than the footprints of a sheepdog?'

'Yes, Mr Holmes, much larger. They were not the prints of an ordinary dog.'

'Also, you say that Sir Charles ran away from this dog? How do you know?' asked Holmes.

'The ground was soft,' answered Dr Mortimer. 'I saw Sir Charles' footprints outside Baskerville Hall. His footprints were close together as he walked along a path at the edge of the moor. Then he stopped and waited by a wooden gate. After that his footprints changed – they became wide apart and deep. I am sure he began to run. He ran towards the house. I believe that something came from the moor. I believe he saw the Hound of the Baskervilles.'

'Yes, yes,' said Holmes, 'but how do you know that Sir Charles waited by this wooden gate?'

'Because he smoked a cigar,' said Dr Mortimer. 'I saw the white cigar ash on the ground.'

'Good,' said Holmes, 'good – you are a detective.'

'Thank you,' said Dr Mortimer, with a smile.

'But you believe that Sir Charles was killed by a gigantic hound?'

'I know he ran away from something,' said Dr Mortimer. 'I know I saw those strange footprints of a huge dog. But . . .' He looked at his watch. '. . . I am meeting Sir Henry Baskerville at Waterloo Station in an hour. Sir Henry is Sir Charles' nephew. He has come from Canada. Sir Charles had no children, so Sir Henry is now the owner of Baskerville Hall. And now I have a problem.'

'What is your problem?' asked Holmes.

'I believe that Sir Henry is in danger,' said Dr Mortimer. 'Is it safe to take him to Baskerville Hall?'

'I must think,' said Sherlock Holmes. 'Stay in London tonight. Come and see me again tomorrow morning. Please bring Sir Henry with you.'

'I shall do so,' said Dr Mortimer. He stood up. 'Now I must go to meet Sir Henry at Waterloo Station. Good day.'

When Dr Mortimer had left, Holmes said to me, 'We have a problem here, Watson. There are three questions. What is the crime? Who did it? How was it done?'

'I believe he saw the Hound of the Baskervilles.'

Sir Henry Baskerville

The next morning, Dr Mortimer brought Sir Henry Baskerville to Baker Street. Sir Henry was about thirty years old. He was not tall, but he was broad and strong. He looked like a boxer.

'How do you do, Mr Holmes,' said Sir Henry. 'I arrived in London yesterday and two strange things have happened already.'

'Please sit down, Sir Henry,' said Holmes. 'Tell me what has happened.'

'No one knows that I am staying at the Northumberland Hotel,' said Sir Henry. 'But I have received a letter. Here is the letter. You see, the words are cut from a newspaper except for the word "moor".'

YOUR LIFE IS IN DANGER KEEP AWAY FROM THE *Moor*

'The words are cut from *The Times* newspaper,' said Holmes.

'But how did this person know where I am staying?' asked Sir Henry.

'I do not know,' said Holmes. 'But you said that two strange things have happened. What is the other strange thing?'

'I have lost a boot,' said Sir Henry. 'Someone has stolen one of my boots at the hotel.'

'One of your boots?' asked Holmes. 'Someone took only one?'

'Yes,' answered Sir Henry. 'The boots are new. I bought them yesterday and I have never worn them. But why take only one?'

'That is a very good question,' said Holmes. 'I would like to visit your hotel. Perhaps I shall find the answer.'

'Then, please join us for lunch,' said Sir Henry. 'Now, if you will excuse me, I have some other business. Shall we meet at two o'clock for lunch at the Northumberland Hotel?'

'We shall come at two,' said Holmes.

Sir Henry Baskerville and Dr Mortimer left the house and walked along Baker Street. Sherlock Holmes watched them through the window of his study.

'Quick, Watson, we must follow them,' said Holmes.

I put on my hat and followed Holmes into the street. 'Why are we following them?' I asked in surprise.

'Because, my dear Watson, someone else is also following them,' said Holmes. 'Look! There is the man. There in that cab!'

I looked where Holmes was pointing. A horse-drawn cab was moving slowly along the street. A man with a black beard was sitting in the cab. He was watching Sir Henry and Dr Mortimer as they walked towards Oxford Street.

A man with a black beard was sitting in the cab.
He was watching Sir Henry and Dr Mortimer.

The man with the black beard turned round as Holmes pointed at him. He saw us and shouted to the cab driver, 'Drive! Drive quickly!' The cab driver whipped the horse and the cab disappeared round a corner.

'I think we have the answer to one of our questions,' said Holmes. 'That man with the black beard followed Sir Henry to the Northumberland Hotel. He is the man who sent the letter.'

5

The Stolen Boot

We arrived at the Northumberland Hotel at ten minutes to two. Sir Henry Baskerville was talking to the hotel manager.

'Two boots in two days,' Sir Henry said loudly. 'Two boots have disappeared from my room – one new boot and one old boot.'

'We shall look everywhere, sir,' said the manager. 'We shall find your stolen boots.'

Sir Henry was silent while we ate lunch. He was angry about his stolen boots.

'Tell me, Mr Holmes,' said Dr Mortimer. 'Is it safe for Sir Henry to go to Baskerville Hall?'

'It is safer than staying in London,' said Holmes. 'Do you know that a man followed you this morning?'

'Followed us!' said Dr Mortimer in surprise. 'Who followed us?'

'A man with a thick black beard,' said Holmes. 'Do you know a man with a black beard?'

'Yes, I do,' replied Dr Mortimer. 'The servant at Baskerville Hall has a thick black beard. His name is Barrymore. I can't think why he is following us. But I am sure Sir Henry is in danger. It is better if Sir Henry stays here in London.'

'No. You are wrong,' said Holmes. 'There are millions of people in London. We cannot watch them all. There are not as many people on Dartmoor. Everyone will notice someone who is a stranger.'

'But this man may not be a stranger,' said Dr Mortimer.

'I agree,' said Holmes. 'That is why Sir Henry must not stay at Baskerville Hall alone. I myself will be busy in London, but my good friend Dr Watson will go with you to Dartmoor.'

'Oh . . . yes, of course,' I said, 'I will certainly go to Dartmoor.'

'Thank you, Dr Watson,' said Sir Henry. 'You will be very welcome at Baskerville Hall.'

'Good,' said Holmes. 'Now, Sir Henry, tell me about the other boot which has been stolen.'

'It is one of an old pair of boots,' said Sir Henry.

'How strange,' said Holmes. 'And, tell me Sir Henry, if you die, who will become the owner of Baskerville Hall?'

'I don't know,' replied Sir Henry. 'Sir Charles had two brothers – my father, who went to Canada, and a younger brother called Roger. But Roger never married and he died in South America. I have no living relatives. I don't know who will get all my money if I die today.'

'And, may I ask, how much money do you have?'

'Certainly, Mr Holmes. Sir Charles left me a fortune of one million pounds,' said Sir Henry.

'Many men will murder their best friend for a million pounds,' said Holmes.

6

Baskerville Hall

On Saturday morning, Sherlock Holmes came with me to Paddington Station.

'This is a dangerous business, Watson,' he said. 'Stay near to Sir Henry. Do not let him walk on the moor alone at night.'

'Don't worry, Holmes,' I said. 'I have brought my army revolver.'

'Good,' said Holmes. 'Write to me every day. Tell me what you see and hear. Tell me all the facts – everything.'

I said goodbye to Sherlock Holmes and met Sir Henry Baskerville and Dr Mortimer at the station. The train journey to Devon took three hours. We looked out of the windows at the green countryside. At last, we reached Dartmoor. Then the countryside changed from green to grey and we saw broken hills of black rock.

We got off the train at the small station in Grimpen Village. A driver was waiting with a carriage and horses to take us to Baskerville Hall. As we rode along the narrow country road, I saw a soldier on a horse. The soldier was carrying a gun and was watching the road.

I spoke to the driver. 'Why is that soldier guarding the road? Is there some trouble?'

'Why is that soldier guarding the road? Is there some trouble?'
'Yes, sir,' the driver replied.

'Yes, sir,' the driver replied. 'A prisoner has escaped from Dartmoor Prison. He's a very dangerous man. His name is Selden. He is a dangerous murderer.'

I looked across the empty moor. A cold wind blew and made me shiver. Holmes believed that someone wanted to murder Sir Henry Baskerville. Now, another murderer was out on the moor. I felt that this lonely place was very dangerous. I wanted to go back to London.

There were thick trees all round Baskerville Hall. It looked like a castle. It stood alone on the empty moor.

We stopped outside Baskerville Hall. 'I must leave you here,' said Dr Mortimer. 'I have a lot of work to do. And my wife is waiting for me at home.'

'I hope you will come to dinner very soon,' said Sir Henry.

'I will,' said Dr Mortimer. 'And if you ever need me, send for me at any time – day or night.' Then Dr Mortimer rode away in the carriage.

A man with a thick black beard and a pale face came out of the house. He greeted Sir Henry.

'Welcome to Baskerville Hall, sir. I am Barrymore. I have been a servant here for many years. My wife and I have prepared the house for you. Shall I show you around the house?'

'Yes please, Barrymore,' said Sir Henry. 'This is Dr Watson. He will be my guest for a few days.'

'Very good, sir,' said Barrymore. He took our cases into the house.

I looked carefully at Barrymore. Was he the man with a black beard who had followed Sir Henry in London? I was not sure.

Mr and Mrs Barrymore had looked after the house well.

Everything was in order. But the house was a cold and lonely place. There was trouble here.

That night I wrote a letter to Sherlock Holmes. I told him all that I had seen and heard. While I was writing, I heard a sound – a woman crying. The only woman in the house was Mrs Barrymore. I wondered why she was so unhappy.

7

The Stapletons of Merripit House

At breakfast next morning, I asked Sir Henry, 'Did you hear a woman crying in the night?'

'I heard a sound like crying,' said Sir Henry. 'But I thought it was the wind on the moor.'

Sir Henry had many papers to read. I left him sitting at his desk and went for a walk on the moor.

I walked for two or three miles across the empty moor. Then, behind me, I heard a voice call, 'Dr Watson!' I looked round. I thought it was Dr Mortimer. But I saw a stranger walking towards me.

'My name is Stapleton,' said the man. 'How do you do, Dr Watson. I saw Dr Mortimer this morning and he told me your name. I have heard about you. You are the friend of the famous detective, Sherlock Holmes, aren't you?'

'Yes, Mr Stapleton, I am,' I said.

'And is Mr Holmes staying at Baskerville Hall too?' asked Stapleton. 'Is he interested in Dartmoor?'

'Mr Holmes is in London,' I said. 'He is a busy man.'

'Of course,' said Stapleton. 'Please come and see my

house. It's very near here. I live with my sister.'

Stapleton led me along a narrow path across a wide, flat part of the moor. The land around us was a strange, green colour. We walked towards a hill of grey rock.

'Be very careful, Dr Watson,' said Stapleton. 'Stay on the path. We are in the Great Grimpen Mire. There is a sea of soft mud underneath the grass. If you fall in, you will never get out again.'

'Thank you for telling me,' I said. 'But why do you live here? It is a dangerous and lonely place.'

'I am a naturalist. I study nature,' said Stapleton. 'There are many interesting flowers and birds on the Great Grimpen Mire. And there are some unusual animals on Dartmoor.'

At that moment we heard a strange sound. It was a deep howling sound – the sound of a large dog. It came from some distance away.

'Stapleton! Is that the sound of a dog?' I asked.

'It is only the sound of the wind,' said Stapleton. 'The wind blows through the rocks and makes strange sounds. But here is my house – Merripit House on the moor.' He pointed to the long, low farmhouse which we could see near the hill. 'And my sister is coming to meet us.'

Miss Stapleton was a very attractive woman. She was slim and tall, with beautiful dark eyes. I thought she looked very different from her brother. She had dark hair, but her brother had fair hair. They were both about thirty years old. Stapleton looked a little older. He was a small, thin, clean-shaven man, with a long face.

'How do you do, Miss Stapleton,' I said. 'Your brother has told me about the Great Grimpen Mire and the unusual flowers and birds. Did you hear that strange sound a moment ago? Does the wind often make this sound?'

I thought Miss Stapleton looked very different from her brother.

'I heard nothing,' Miss Stapleton said quickly. She looked at her brother and I saw fear in her eyes.

Her brother looked at her angrily. 'Let us show Dr Watson our house,' he said.

I stayed for a short time. Stapleton showed me his collection of flowers and butterflies.

'I will come to Baskerville Hall to visit Sir Henry this afternoon,' said Stapleton. 'Will you tell him?'

'Of course,' I replied. 'Now, if you will excuse me, I must go back to Baskerville Hall. I hope to see you again soon.'

'Stay on the path,' said Stapleton. 'Remember the Great Grimpen Mire. Many men have died in it.'

Miss Stapleton walked outside with me. She spoke quickly, in a quiet voice. 'Dr Watson, I want to tell you about the strange sound you heard. The people here say that it is the sound of the Hound of the Baskervilles. They say it killed Sir Charles and now it will kill Sir Henry. But, please, do not tell my brother that I spoke to you. Now, go back to London. Go back today!'

She went into the house quickly. I walked along the narrow path slowly, thinking about what she had said.

8

Dr Watson's First Report

Baskerville Hall

Dartmoor

13 October 1889

My Dear Holmes,

I wrote and told you about Baskerville Hall and the people who live here. Now I have more facts to tell you. First, I will draw a map of the area. It will help you to understand my story.

Baskerville Hall is about two miles south-west of Grimpen Village. I walk to the village to post letters.

There are trees all round the Hall and a long avenue leads to a small summer-house in the garden. Sir Charles Baskerville died near the summer-house. I have marked the gate on the map. It is where Sir Charles stood and smoked a cigar. The gate opens onto the moor.

I have told you about the neighbours. Dr Mortimer lives nearby, about half-way between the villages of Grimpen and Coombe Tracey.

I have met the Stapletons. Their house is about three miles from the Hall. It is on the other side of High Tor.

There is one man I have not met. But Dr Mortimer has told me about him. His name is Mr Frankland and he lives at Lafter Hall. He has a large telescope and is interested in astronomy. He uses his telescope to look at the stars.

In the past few days, he has not looked at the stars. He has looked at the moor. He is watching the moor because the police have not caught the murderer, Selden. Mr Frankland

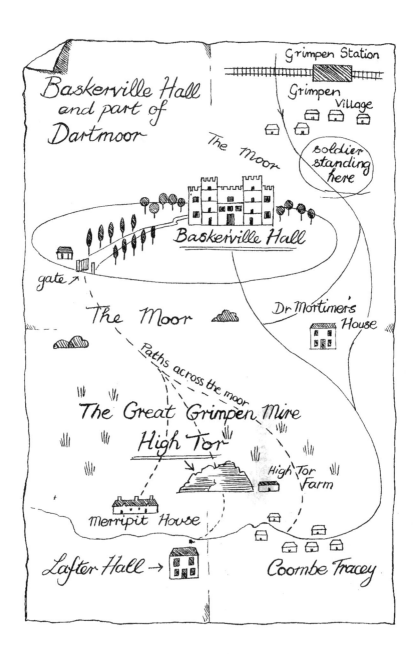

watches the moor looking for strangers. But I do not think that Selden is hiding on the moor. There is no food and the weather is now very cold.

Sir Henry is worried about the Stapletons. He thinks that the murderer may break into their house. He has visited Miss Stapleton several times and they have become good friends. But Mr Stapleton is a strange man. He does not like Sir Henry visiting his sister.

Now, here is some news about Barrymore, the servant at Baskerville Hall. He looks like the man we saw in the carriage in London. You remember – the man who followed Sir Henry and Dr Mortimer to Baker Street. I told Sir Henry what I thought and he called Barrymore and asked him, 'Have you been to London recently?'

Barrymore says he has never been to London in his life Also, Sir Henry's question made him angry. He said he wanted to leave Baskerville Hall.

Sir Henry said he was sorry. He gave Barrymore some clothes and Barrymore was pleased. Barrymore and his wife thanked Sir Henry very much for the clothes.

Then, last night, I saw something very strange. In the middle of the night I heard footsteps and I looked out of my bedroom door. I saw Barrymore with a candle. I saw him walk to the end of the corridor. He stopped at the large window which looks out over the moor. He held the candle to the window and moved it backwards and forwards.

I went to the window of my own room and looked out across the moor. I saw a light moving backwards and forwards. It was somewhere near High Tor and it was clearly a signal. But a signal for what?

The Light On The Moor

Baskerville Hall

Dartmoor

15 October 1889

My Dear Holmes,

I am now able to answer the question at the end of my last letter. I know why Barrymore signalled with a candle.

First, let me tell you about Sir Henry and Miss Stapleton. I told you that they are very friendly. I have found out that Sir Henry is in love with her. The truth is he wants to marry her.

Yesterday morning he said to me, 'I am going to see Miss Stapleton. I want to go alone.'

'But Mr Holmes told me to stay with you,' I said. 'You must not go across the moor on your own.'

'I shall go alone,' said Sir Henry, and he went out.

I did not know what to do. I waited for ten minutes, then I decided to follow him. I did not see everything, but this is what happened.

Sir Henry met Miss Stapleton on the moor. He asked her to marry him – he told me this afterwards. They walked towards Merripit House to see Mr Stapleton. They met him outside the house. Sir Henry told Stapleton the news.

I reached High Tor before Sir Henry met Stapleton, so I saw what happened next. I saw Sir Henry talking to Stapleton. Suddenly Stapleton became wild and angry. He shouted at Sir Henry. Then he took his sister's hand and pulled her towards Merripit House.

Sir Henry turned away and walked back towards the Hall. He saw me by High Tor. He was not angry that I had followed him.

'Watson,' he said, 'that man is mad. I told him that I want to marry his sister. He shouted at me. He told me never to see her again. I think he is mad.'

I said nothing and we walked back to the Hall. That afternoon, Stapleton came to the Hall. He wanted to speak to Sir Henry. He kept saying, 'I am sorry. I was very rude.' Then he invited Sir Henry to dinner at Merripit House on Friday night.

Now I will tell you the story of Barrymore. I told Sir Henry that I had seen Barrymore signal with a candle. Sir Henry said, 'We will wait for him tonight. If he signals again, we will catch him.'

Sir Henry and I did not go to bed. We sat waiting in Sir Henry's study until two o'clock in the morning. Then we heard footsteps outside the study. We listened. The footsteps went upstairs.

Sir Henry and I waited for two more minutes. Then we opened the door quietly, and went upstairs. We saw Barrymore by the large window at the end of the corridor. He had a candle in his hand and he was waving the candle in front of the window.

'What are you doing, Barrymore?' Sir Henry shouted.

Barrymore almost dropped the candle. He looked frightened. 'Nothing, Sir Henry,' he said. 'I'm checking the window, that's all.'

'You are signalling to someone on the moor,' said Sir Henry. 'Who is outside? Tell me!'

'No one, sir,' said Barrymore.

'Tell me,' said Sir Henry, 'or you shall leave this house

tomorrow. Tell me now!'

'Sir Henry,' said another voice, 'please don't be angry with my husband. It is my fault.'

We turned and saw Mrs Barrymore. She was standing at the top of the stairs, holding her hands tightly together.

'My brother is outside, sir,' she said. 'My brother is Selden, the man who escaped from prison.'

'Selden – the murderer?' I said. 'And why do you signal to him at night?'

'My husband takes him food and clothes,' said Mrs Barrymore. 'We signal to tell him my husband is coming.'

'I understand,' said Sir Henry. 'He is your brother; you must try to help him. Go to your room. We will talk about this in the morning.'

The Barrymores left the room.

Sir Henry turned and spoke to me. 'I am sorry for them, but Selden is a murderer. I must try to catch him.'

'Look!' I said. 'Look out of the window. There is a light on the moor.'

Sir Henry looked. A small light was shining on the moor. It was near High Tor.

'That's him!' said Sir Henry. 'Come, Dr Watson, we will go to that light. Bring your revolver.'

We put on our coats quickly and went out onto the moor. The moon was bright and so we could see the path across the moor. Also, we could see the signal light. It was about a mile away.

'There!' said Sir Henry. 'Selden is there. Hurry!'

I followed Sir Henry along the path across the moor. I was worried. I did not want Sir Henry to go far on the moor at night.

'Sir Henry,' said Mrs Barrymore, 'please don't be angry
with my husband. It is my fault.'

At that moment, we heard a strange sound. It was a deep howling sound. It came from some distance away.

'What's that?' asked Sir Henry. There was fear in his voice.

I was afraid too. 'It sounds like a dog,' I said. 'It sounds like a very large dog. Shall we turn back?'

'No,' said Sir Henry. 'We are nearly there. Look!'

In front of us, we saw the signal light clearly. It came from a lamp which stood on a rock. Beside the rock was a man, but the man did not see us. He was looking in the other direction.

Again we heard that deep howling sound – the sound of a huge dog. The sound was much nearer now. We heard the sound again. It was coming nearer all the time! The man by the rock heard the sound as well. He picked up the lantern and jumped on the rock. He looked one way, then the other. Suddenly he jumped off the rock and started to run.

He ran towards High Tor. He was running away from us. But he was not running away because he saw us. He was running away from something else which we could not see.

'Quick, Dr Watson, follow him!' shouted Sir Henry. 'Get your revolver ready.'

We ran along the narrow path. Near us, we heard the deep howling sound. It was very near and very loud. Then we heard a scream. We stopped.

'Be careful, Dr Watson,' said Sir Henry. 'Let us go forward slowly.'

The night was silent. We walked forward slowly. There was something, or someone, lying near the bottom of the Tor. We went over to it. I held my revolver in front of me.

We found the body of a man at the foot of the Tor.

We found the body of a man at the foot of the Tor.

The man had fallen from the rocky hill. He was dead. His neck was broken.

We were sure that the man was Selden. He was dressed in Sir Henry's old clothes – the clothes that Sir Henry had given to Barrymore.

I have one last strange thing to tell you, Holmes.

I looked up at the Tor from which Selden had fallen. Up above, at the top of the Tor, stood a tall, thin man. I saw him only for a moment. Then he disappeared into the night. But I know I have seen him before. I will search for this strange man who walks on the moor at night.

10

The Man On The Moor

Who was the man I had seen on High Tor? Was it the man Holmes and I had seen in London? But I was sure that the man on High Tor did not have a beard. Sir Henry did not see the man on the Tor and I said nothing to him.

There was nothing we could do for Selden. We went back to the house. What had Selden run away from? What had he seen? What had we heard? Was it the Hound of the Baskervilles? I felt safer in Baskerville Hall than out on the moor at night. Sir Henry felt the same.

In the morning, we sent for the police. They took Selden's body away.

Sir Henry told the Barrymores what had happened. But he did not speak about the strange sounds we had heard. Mrs Barrymore cried and covered her face with a handkerchief. Mr Barrymore said, 'It had to end. Poor Selden could not have lived on the moor in winter. It is far too cold.'

'Please forget what I said last night,' Sir Henry told them. 'I want you to stay at Baskerville Hall.'

'Thank you, sir. We will,' said Barrymore.

I went to my room and wrote a long report to Sherlock Holmes. Then I decided to go for a walk, but I did not want to walk on the moor. I did not like the moor.

Usually, I posted my letters to Holmes in Grimpen Village. But today I decided to walk to Coombe Tracey, the village to the south. It took me an hour to walk there along the road. On the way, I saw Stapleton.

'I heard you caught the escaped murderer,' said Stapleton. 'I will look forward to hearing the story from Sir Henry at dinner tomorrow.'

'Sir Henry is looking forward to dining with you and your sister tomorrow,' I replied.

'And so is my sister,' Stapleton said coldly. 'I look forward to seeing Sir Henry tomorrow at eight o'clock.'

'I will tell him,' I said. 'Good day.'

I walked on to Coombe Tracey and posted my letter. I saw a large house outside the village and asked who lived there.

'That is Mr Frankland's house,' the village shopkeeper told me.

Dr Mortimer had told me about Mr Frankland – and about Mr Frankland's interest in the stars. I decided to visit the gentleman and ask to see his telescope.

Mr Frankland was standing by his garden gate. He was a red-faced, elderly man with white hair.

'Good day,' I said, 'my name is Watson.'

'Dr Watson?' asked Mr Frankland.

'Yes,' I replied.

'I heard that you caught Selden last night on the moor,' said Mr Frankland. 'I nearly caught him myself.'

'How did you do that?' I asked in surprise.

'With my telescope. Come and see.'

Mr Frankland showed me into his house. I was very interested in his telescope. It was very large and powerful.

'I saw a man on the moor a number of times,' said Mr Frankland.

'Why did you not tell the police?' I asked.

'I was not sure that it was the murderer,' he replied. 'I began to think that perhaps there were two men on the moor. But why would anyone want to live out on the moor? There is no food and the weather is cold. Then, yesterday, I saw something.'

'What did you see?' I asked.

'I saw someone taking food out on the moor,' answered Mr Frankland.

'At night?' I asked. I thought of Barrymore and his signal light. Perhaps Mr Frankland had seen Barrymore taking food and clothing out to Selden.

'No,' said Mr Frankland. 'I saw a boy taking food during the day – and letters.'

'Letters?' I asked. 'Are you sure?'

'Very sure,' said Mr Frankland, 'because I know the boy. I asked the postman and learnt that the boy collects letters every day.'

'And where does he take them?' I asked.

'Look through the telescope,' said Mr Frankland. 'Look at that old farmhouse to the right of High Tor. That is High Tor Farm. Someone lives there, but I do not know who. He is a stranger.'

I looked through the telescope at High Tor. On the left of the Tor I saw the roof of Merripit House, where the Stapletons lived. On the right, I saw an old farmhouse. The roof was broken and so was one wall. But I saw smoke coming from the chimney.

'Thank you, Mr Frankland,' I said. 'Whoever lives there is not Selden. Selden is dead.'

I said goodbye to Mr Frankland. Then I decided to walk across the moor and look at old High Tor Farm. It was a mile or two away and I reached it late in the afternoon. The sun was low in the sky and the air was cold.

I walked up to the farmhouse slowly. The door was

41

'Someone lives there, but I do not know who. He is a stranger.'

broken and I looked inside. The farmhouse was empty and silent.

Part of the farmhouse was dry, where the roof was not broken. There was a wood fire on the floor and a bed in the corner. A lamp stood on a table with a pile of papers next to it.

I went into the farmhouse carefully. I put my hand into my jacket pocket where I kept my army revolver. I walked slowly to the table and looked at the pile of papers. I saw one of my own letters. Someone had stolen one of my own letters!

Who lived in the farmhouse? Was it the man with the black beard? Was it the man I had seen on the Tor?

I soon found out, as I heard the sound of footsteps outside. I took my revolver out of my pocket and turned towards the door. A tall, thin man stood in the doorway with his back to the setting sun. I could not see his face.

'It is a lovely evening, isn't it Watson?' the man said.

The man was Sherlock Holmes.

11

High Tor Farm

'Holmes!' I said in surprise. 'What are you doing here?'

'I am watching,' said Holmes. 'I am waiting for the murderer to show himself.'

'The murderer? Do you mean Selden? Selden is dead.'

'I know. I was on the Tor last night and saw what happened,' Holmes said. 'Someone wanted to kill Sir Henry Baskerville, not Selden.'

'But how long have you been here?' I asked. 'And why are you here in secret?'

'I came here on the same day as you,' answered Sherlock Holmes. 'I came in secret because the murderer is clever. He will not show himself if he knows I am here.'

'And what about my letters?' I asked. 'Have you read them?'

'Yes, I have,' Holmes replied. 'They were sent to me from London. But I have not read your report of last night. Come. Tell me about it as we walk to Baskerville Hall.'

He left the farmhouse and I walked quickly after him. The sun had gone down and it was getting dark. A thick white mist was rising from the moor.

'You are a good detective,' said Holmes. 'Tell me, how did you find me? How did you know I was at High Tor Farm?'

'I did not know it was you,' I answered. 'Mr Frankland saw you through his telescope. And he saw the boy who brought you food and letters. He thought you were Selden, the murderer. Also, I saw you last night on the Tor.'

'I see,' said Holmes. 'If you saw me, I think the murderer of Sir Charles Baskerville saw me too. He will want to kill me as well as Sir Henry.'

'So,' I said, 'you think that Sir Charles was murdered?'

'I am sure of it,' said Holmes. 'Now, stay on the path.'

It was dark and the moon had not come up. We had to walk carefully. The path went through the Great Grimpen Mire and a sea of soft mud lay under the grass on either side of us.

Behind us, we heard that strange sound, the deep howling sound I had heard on the moor last night. It made me shiver with fear.

'What is it, Holmes?' I asked. 'Do you know what makes that sound.'

'No,' he answered, 'but the village people say it is the Hound of the Baskervilles. I will not go back to High Tor Farm tonight. Come. We must hurry. Keep your revolver ready.'

We walked quickly along the dark path. I was pleased to see the lights of Baskerville Hall in front of us. I was afraid of what was behind us – out on the moor, at night.

12

Setting the Trap

'Mr Sherlock Holmes,' said Sir Henry Baskerville, 'what a surprise! Welcome to Baskerville Hall.'

'Thank you,' said Holmes. 'But you did not obey my orders. Last night you went out on the moor. You were nearly murdered!'

'But I did not go alone,' said Sir Henry. 'Dr Watson was with me. He has a revolver to protect me.'

'And I shall protect you too,' said Holmes. 'Next time you go out on the moor at night, both Dr Watson and I will go with you.'

'The next time . . .' Sir Henry began.

'The next time will be tomorrow night,' said Holmes. 'Dr Watson tells me that you are going to dinner at Merripit House on the moor. I believe the Stapletons have invited you.'

'Yes,' Sir Henry said. 'And has Dr Watson told you that I want to marry Miss Stapleton?'

'Yes, he has,' said Holmes. 'Now I would like to ask Barrymore some questions.'

Sir Henry called for his servant, Barrymore. Barrymore came and stood in front of us. Sherlock Holmes looked at him carefully. Was this the man with the black beard we had seen in London?

'Tell me about Sir Charles Baskerville,' Holmes said to Barrymore. 'Did he often go for a walk at night?'

'No, sir,' said Barrymore, 'Sir Charles did not often leave the house at night.'

'But, on the night he died, he went for a walk on the edge of the moor,' said Holmes. 'We know he stood by the gate on the edge of the moor for about ten minutes. Was he waiting for someone?'

'I'm not sure, sir,' said Barrymore. 'I remember that Sir Charles received a letter that day.'

'A letter?' Holmes asked. 'Why do you remember this letter? Did you read it?'

'No, sir,' Barrymore said. 'I never read Sir Charles' letters. But Sir Charles usually kept his letters on his desk. This letter was unusual. He read it. Then he put it on the fire.'

'Oh, so he burnt it,' Holmes said. 'Perhaps this letter asked him to meet someone. Perhaps he went to this meeting and met someone – or something.'

'But why did Sir Charles burn the letter?' I asked.

'Why do people burn letters, Watson?' asked Holmes. 'Often because they have something to hide. But Sir Charles was afraid to go out on the moor at night. Dr Mortimer told us that Sir Charles believed the story of the

46

Hound of the Baskervilles. Why would he go out on the moor, alone, at night? If he was going to meet someone, it was someone he knew. But why meet on the edge of the moor? Was it a secret meeting?'

'Do you think Sir Charles was murdered by a friend?' I asked.

'I think he knew his murderer,' replied Holmes. 'And I think his murderer is not far away.'

After dinner, we sat in the library. There were paintings of the Baskerville family hanging on the walls. Some of the paintings were very old.

Sherlock Holmes looked at the paintings carefully. He was interested in the painting of Sir Hugo Baskerville, dated 1645.

'Interesting, Watson, very interesting,' said Holmes. 'Here is a painting of Sir Hugo, the man who started the story of the Hound of the Baskervilles. I am able to remember faces. Look at this black beard and the face. Have you seen this face before?'

'Yes, Holmes,' I said. 'It is the face of the man we saw in London. It is the man who followed Sir Henry in a cab!'

Sherlock Holmes was interested in the painting of
Sir Hugo Baskerville, dated 1645.

The Hound of the Baskervilles

Holmes got up early the next morning. He went to Grimpen Village and sent a telegram. When he returned to Baskerville Hall he was excited. 'We shall go hunting tonight,' he said, 'and Inspector Lestrade from Scotland Yard will come with us.'

'Why are we waiting until tonight?' I asked. 'You know who the murderer is, Holmes. Why can't we catch him before tonight?'

'We must make sure we have the right man,' Holmes said. 'We must wait. We will catch him tonight!'

Inspector Lestrade arrived from London at five o'clock. We met him at Grimpen Station. He was a short man, with bright eyes. He and Sherlock Holmes were good friends. He and Holmes talked together as we drove to Baskerville Hall.

At half past seven, when Sir Henry left the Hall, we were ready.

Sir Henry walked along the path across the Great Grimpen Mire, towards Merripit House. The Stapletons had asked him to come to dinner at eight o'clock.

The three of us followed him – Lestrade, Holmes and I. Each of us carried a revolver. We saw Sir Henry go into Merripit House. We waited below High Tor, about two hundred yards from the house.

The lights burned brightly in Merripit House and the curtains of the dining room were open. We saw Sir Henry talking to Stapleton.

'Where is Miss Stapleton?' I said to Holmes. 'Sir Henry has come to see her, not her brother.'

'Perhaps Stapleton wants to talk to Sir Henry alone,' Holmes said. 'But, look – the mist is rising. Soon we will not be able to see.'

I looked around. Thick white mist was rising from the Great Grimpen Mire.

'Shall we climb up the Tor?' I asked. 'Perhaps we will be able to see better from above the mist.'

We climbed a little way up the Tor. But the mist was so thick we could only see a few yards in front of us.

'I did not think of this,' said Holmes. 'Our plan may fail if we cannot see clearly. We must listen for any sounds from Merripit House.'

We waited in the mist and the moon came up. The white moonlight shone through the mist, but we could not see Merripit House or the path across the moor.

We listened. At last we heard a door open, then the sound of voices. Stapleton was saying goodnight to Sir Henry. Then we heard footsteps below the Tor. Someone was walking along a stony part of the path.

At the same time, we heard another sound. It was the sound of a metal chain and came from Merripit House. Then we heard the deep howling sound of a huge dog.

'The Hound!' Holmes shouted. 'Sir Henry! Sir Henry! Climb the Tor! We are here on the Tor! Hurry!'

Lestrade moved forward to help Sir Henry. But we could not see clearly in the mist.

'Keep back!' Holmes shouted to Lestrade.

Lestrade cried out and fired his revolver into the mist. We saw the yellow flash of the revolver and we heard the loud bang. 'It's coming!' Lestrade cried out. He fired again.

In the light of the flash, we saw a huge black shape.

In the light of the flash, we saw a huge black shape.

Its eyes and jaws were burning bright with fire. It was a horrible huge monster. It ran past Lestrade. We heard Sir Henry cry out.

We heard the sound of falling stones.

Holmes and I both fired our revolvers at the black shape. We heard a howl. We fired again and again. Then we moved forward carefully and climbed down the Tor.

Sir Henry was at the bottom of the Tor. He had fallen, but he was not hurt. He now stood up carefully.

'What was it, Mr Holmes?' he asked. 'What was that thing in the mist?'

Holmes walked along the path, reloading his revolver with bullets. 'We are safe,' he called back. 'The dog is dead.'

I went to look. There on the path lay the largest black dog I have ever seen. Fire burned around the dog's eyes and mouth. Blood was pouring from its head.

'Could it have killed Sir Henry?' I asked.

'It would have frightened him,' said Holmes. 'The path across the Great Grimpen Mire is narrow. If he had run in the dark, Sir Henry would have fallen into the mire and died.'

'But where did it come from?' I asked. 'And why is its head burning with fire?'

'I believe it was kept in Merripit House,' said Holmes. 'The fire is easy to explain.'

He touched the dog's head with his fingers. 'It is a special paint,' he said. 'Come. Let us find the murderer.'

We walked back to Merripit House. The door was open. Sir Henry went into the house. 'Miss Stapleton!' he shouted. 'Where is she? She did not join us for dinner.'

A sound came from one of the rooms. Sir Henry pushed

the door open. Miss Stapleton lay on the bed. Her hands and feet were tied together. There was a cloth tied across her mouth.

Sir Henry cut the rope around her hands. Holmes took the cloth from her mouth.

'Where is your brother, Miss Stapleton?' Sir Henry asked.

Miss Stapleton looked at the floor. 'Gone,' she said. 'My husband has gone.'

'Your husband!' shouted Sir Henry. 'You are Mrs Stapleton?'

'Yes, I am his wife,' she said. 'But his name is not Stapleton. He is the son of your dead uncle, Roger Baskerville. He is your cousin.'

Out on the moor we heard a terrible cry. We ran outside. The mist was thick on the Great Grimpen Mire. The cry came again, and then a loud scream. Then silence.

'I believe that the Great Grimpen Mire has taken your cousin,' Holmes said to Sir Henry. 'He has fallen into the mire. We shall never find his body.'

14

Back In Baker Street

'There are still some things I don't understand,' I said to Holmes. 'Tell me – who was Stapleton? Why did he want to kill Sir Henry?'

'It is simple, my dear Watson,' said Holmes. 'Remember Sir Charles had two brothers. The youngest brother, Roger, was a bad man. He got into trouble over money and went to

South America. He died in Venezuela. He did not marry, so no one knew he had a son.'

'And this son called himself Stapleton?'

'Yes, and the son was both bad and clever. He wanted the Baskerville money. There were only two Baskervilles left alive – Sir Charles and Sir Henry. If they died, Baskerville Hall would belong to Stapleton.'

'What about his wife? Why did Stapleton say she was his sister?'

'At first, Stapleton wanted her to marry Sir Charles or Sir Henry. That was a way of getting the money.'

'What an evil man!' I said. 'But she did not want to help Stapleton. She tried to warn both of them, didn't she?'

'Yes, she tried to meet Sir Charles the night he died. But Stapleton found out. Stapleton waited for Sir Charles and frightened him to death with the black dog. Also, Mrs Stapleton sent the note to Sir Henry at the Northumberland Hotel. Then Sir Henry fell in love with Mrs Stapleton, so Stapleton was worried and angry. At last, Stapleton had to tie her up to stop her telling Sir Henry.'

'And Stapleton was the man with the black beard?'

'Yes, he tried to hide his face. He put on a beard when he followed Sir Henry in London.'

'What about the missing boots?' I asked.

'The dog and the boots go together,' Holmes said. 'Stapleton knew the silly story about the Hound of the Baskervilles. And he knew that Sir Charles believed the story. So, Stapleton bought that huge black dog and let it walk on the moor at night.'

'But the boots,' I said. 'What about the stolen boots?'

'Watson, you are very slow,' said Holmes. 'It was a hunting dog. Hunting dogs will follow a smell. Stapleton wanted some of Sir Henry's clothes to give to the dog. He paid a waiter at the hotel to steal the boots. But the first boot did not work because it was new. It did not have Sir Henry's smell. Then, remember, the dog hunted Selden because Selden was wearing Sir Henry's old clothes.'

'What a strange story,' I said. 'Stapleton was clever.'

'Yes, my dear Watson,' said Holmes. 'I needed your help to catch him. Now, why don't you write about it? Perhaps you can call your story *The Case of the Stolen Boot?'*

POINTS
FOR
UNDERSTANDING

Points For Understanding

1

1 Who is telling this story?
2 What is Sherlock Holmes' address?
3 Why had Dr Mortimer come to visit Holmes?

2

1 Where does Dr Mortimer live?
2 Who was Sir Charles Baskerville?
3 What had happened to Sir Charles?
4 Tell the story of the Curse of the Hound of the Baskervilles.
5 Did Sherlock Holmes believe this story?
6 Where had Dr Mortimer found Sir Charles' body?
7 Dr Mortimer found many footprints on the ground.
  How had these footprints been made?

3

1 What had happened to the footprints?
2 How did Dr Mortimer know Sir Charles had waited by the wooden gate?
3 Dr Mortimer is meeting Sir Henry Baskerville.
  (a) Who is he?
  (b) Where is he meeting him?
  (c) Where has he been living?
4 Where did Sherlock Holmes tell Dr Mortimer to stay that night?
5 What did Sherlock Holmes tell Dr Mortimer to do the next day?
6 'There are three questions,' said Holmes. What are the three questions?

4

1 How old was Sir Henry? What did he look like?
2 Sir Henry had received a letter that morning. Describe the letter and say why it was unusual.
3 What strange thing had happened when Sir Henry was in his hotel bedroom?
4 'Quick, Watson, we must follow him.'
    (a)   Who did Holmes and Watson follow?
    (b)   Why did they follow him?
5 Who sent the letter to Sir Henry Baskerville?

5

1 Why was Sir Henry angry at lunch?
2 Why did Holmes think it was safer for Sir Henry to go to Dartmoor than to stay in London?
3 Holmes wanted someone to go with Sir Henry to Baskerville Hall. Who was this?
4 Who will become the owner of Baskerville Hall if Sir Henry dies?
5 How much money did Sir Henry have?

6

1 Holmes told Watson to stay near to Sir Henry.
    (a)   What must Sir Henry not do at night?
    (b)   What had Watson brought with him?
2 On the way to Baskerville Hall, Watson saw a soldier guarding the road. Why was the soldier guarding the road?
3 Why did Watson want to go back to London?
4 Why did Dr Mortimer leave Sir Henry and Watson?
5 'I am Barrymore,' said the man.
    (a)   Who was Barrymore?
    (b)   Describe Barrymore.
    (c)   Did Watson think he had seen Barrymore before?
6 What did Watson hear at night while he was writing a letter to Holmes?

7

1 Who did Stapleton say he lived with?
2 What happened to anyone who fell in the Great Grimpen Mire?
3 As Watson and Stapleton were walking to Stapleton's house, they heard a strange sound.
    (a)   What did Watson say made the sound?
    (b)   What did Stapleton say made the sound?
4 Describe Miss Stapleton. Did Watson think she looked like her brother?
5 Miss Stapleton walked outside with Dr Watson.
(a) What did she tell him had made the strange sound?
(b)   What did she tell Watson to do?

8

1 What did Sir Charles do while he stood by the gate?
2 Dr Mortimer told Dr Watson about Mr Frankland.
    (a) Where does Mr Frankland live?
    (b) What does Mr Frankland use to look at the stars?
    (c) Why is Mr Frankland looking at the moor?
3 Who has Sir Henry become good friends with?
4 What question did Sir Henry ask Barrymore? What was Barrymore's reply?
5 What did Sir Henry give Barrymore?
6 What did Dr Watson see in the middle of the night?

9

1 What has Dr Watson found out about Sir Henry?
2 Sir Henry went out onto the moor alone. What did Dr Watson do?
3 What did Sir Henry tell Dr Watson about Stapleton?
4 Who was Barrymore signalling to out on the moor? Why was he sending a signal?
5 Why did Sir Henry and Dr Watson go out onto the moor?
6 What strange sound did they hear?
7 What did Watson and Sir Henry find lying near the bottom of the Tor?
8 What did Dr Watson see for a moment at the top of the Tor?

10

1 Describe the man Dr Watson had seen on top of the Tor.
2 'I saw a man on the moor a number of times,' said Mr Frankland.
    (a) Why did Mr Frankland not tell the police?
    (b) How many men did Mr Frankland begin to think were on the moor?
3 What was the boy taking out on the moor during the day?
4 Where was the boy taking the letters to?
5 Who was the other man on the moor?

11

1 When did Holmes come to Dartmoor?
2 Which other person will the murderer of Sir Henry want to murder?
3 Why was Dr Watson pleased to see the lights of Baskerville Hall?

12

1 'The next time . . .' Sir Henry began.
    (a) When was Sir Henry going out on the moor again?
    (b) Who was going with him?
    (c) Who was Sir Henry going to visit?
2 Barrymore told Holmes that Sir Charles had received a letter on the day he died.
    (a) What did Sir Charles do after he read the letter?
    (b) What did Holmes think was in the letter?
3 Dr Watson asks, 'Do you think Sir Charles was murdered by a friend?' What was Holmes' reply?
4 Holmes pointed to a painting of Sir Hugo Baskerville. What did Holmes think was interesting about the painting?

13

1 Who did Holmes invite to come and join them at Baskerville Hall?

2   Sir Henry walked across the path to Merripit House.
       (a) Who followed behind him?
       (b) What did they each carry?
       (c) Where did Sir Henry go?
       (d) Where did the three wait?
3   Why was Holmes afraid their plan might fail?
4   What sound did they hear coming from Merripit House?
5   Lestrade fired his gun. Describe what they saw in the light of the flash.
6   What had been killed? How had its face been made to burn with fire?
7   Who was 'Miss Stapleton'?
8   What happened to Stapleton?

14

1   Explain who Stapleton was.
2   Why did Stapleton want his wife to marry Sir Henry?
3   Why had Stapleton's wife tried to warn Sir Charles?
4   How had Sir Charles died?
5   Who was the man with the black beard?
6   Explain why two of Sir Henry's boots had been stolen from his hotel in London.
7   Why had the dog hunted the murderer, Selden?

Exercises

Multiple Choice

Tick the best answer.

1 When does this story take place?
a ☑ In the nineteenth century.
b ☐ In the twentieth century.
c ☐ In the twenty-first century.

2 Who was Sherlock Holmes?
a ☐ The man who wrote the story.
b ☐ A famous detective.
c ☐ A famous policeman.

3 Who was Dr Watson?
a ☐ A friend of Sherlock Holmes.
b ☐ A man who lived on Dartmoor.
c ☐ A police officer.

4 What was the Hound of the Baskervilles?
a ☐ A family pet.
b ☐ A family servant.
c ☐ A big black dog.

5 Where was Baskerville Hall?
a ☐ In London.
b ☐ On Dartmoor.
c ☐ In Canada.

6 Who were the Baskervilles?
a ☐ An old and rich family.
b ☐ People who kept dogs.
c ☐ Hotel owners.

7 Who was Sir Charles Baskerville?
a ☐ The man who came to London to see Sherlock Holmes.
b ☐ The man who came from Canada to look after Baskerville Hall.
c ☐ The man who died of a heart attack on Dartmoor.

8 Why was Dr Mortimer worried about Sir Henry Baskerville?
a ☐ Because Sir Henry had just arrived from Canada.
b ☐ Because Sir Henry didn't know that Sir Charles was dead.
c ☐ Because he believed Sir Henry was in danger.

Words From the Story

Complete the gaps. Use each word in the box once.

> howl   Dartmoor Prison   footprints   mire   hound   curse
> gigantic   lanterns   moor   boots   cruel   naturalist
> Dartmoor   candles   revolver

1 .... *Dartmoor* .... is the name of a wild and deserted
area in the south-west of England.

2 A .... is an area of wild land with few
trees. Few people live there.

3 A .... is a dog used for hunting and
racing. In this story it means a very big dog.

4 A .... is a wish for something bad to
happen to someone.

5 A .... is the long loud sound made by a
wolf and some kinds of dog.

6 A .... person likes to hurt other people
and animals.

7 .... means very big – like a giant.

8 .... are marks made in the ground by the feet of men and animals.

9 A .... is a place of soft mud, sometimes covered with grass. It can be dangerous if you fall in.

10 .... are footwear that cover your feet and ankles, and sometimes your legs.

11 .... is an old-fashioned word for a person who studies nature – plants and animals.

12 .... and .... are lights that people used at night before electricity.

13 A .... is a kind of hand gun.

14 .... was a place for keeping very dangerous criminals such as murderers.

A Logic Problem

Read the information. Then complete the tables.

Sherlock Holmes asks some questions at the Northumberland Hotel. He finds out the following:

1 The receptionist says that a page is missing from the hotel register.

2 Three people stayed at the hotel on the same day as Sir Henry.

3 The doorman remembers a Mrs Augusta, a Miss Charlotte, and a Mr Platstone.

4 The housekeeper remembers three pairs of boots – black, brown, and green.

65

5 The maid remembers that the other three people stayed in rooms 18, 19, and 20.

Holmes needs to answer the questions:

a   Who stayed in which room?
b   What colour were their boots?

He draws a table, then he talks to the maid again.

X = No	Black	Brown	Green	Room 18	Room 19	Room 20
Mrs Augusta						
Miss Charlotte						
Mr Platstone						
Room 18						
Room 19						
Room 20						

Maid: 'The two ladies did not stay next to each other. The green boots were muddy and I'm sure they were outside room 20. Miss Charlotte was very clean and tidy. I don't think her boots were muddy. And I don't think the black boots were hers either, because they were a very large size. That's all I can tell you.'

Holmes: 'That is more than enough information, thank you.'

Room	Name	Boots

Sir Hugo and the Curse of the Baskervilles

Complete the gaps. Use each word in the box once.

> hunting   forward   beside   stopped   Devil   dogs   moor
> howling   dog   sound   mouth   shouted   not   afraid
> eyes   horse   gigantic   throat   fell   across
> deaths   girl   teeth   rode   found

The men [1]........*rode*........ their horses [2]... the
moor. Their [3]..................................... dogs ran [4].....................................
them. They did [5]............................. catch the [6]...................................... .
All of a sudden the horses [7]............................. . The [8].............................
stopped. They heard a strange [9]... . It was the
sound of a dog [10]............................. – a very big [11]............................. .

'Cowards!' [12]............................. Sir Hugo. 'Are you [13].............................
of a dog?' He rode his horse [14]..., but the horse
suddenly stopped and Sir Hugo [15].................................. to the ground.

The men saw a [16]... black dog appear in the
moonlight. It had fiery red [17].................................. . It was almost as
big as a [18]... . The dog jumped on Sir Hugo and
tore at his [19] .... The men saw the fiery eyes and
the white [20]... and blood running from the dog's
[21]................................. . They ran away. No one [22]...................................
the body of Sir Hugo Baskerville. People said that the
[23]... took him.

Ever since that time, the Baskervilles have died strange
[24]... . Many have died on the
[25]... . People believe that the gigantic dog
killed them. This dog is the curse: it is called the Hound of the
Baskervilles. Now there is only one Baskerville left alive – Sir Henry.

Dr Watson's Map

Complete the gaps with the correct word from the brackets.

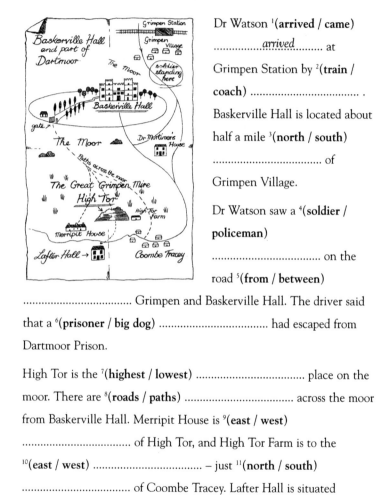

Dr Watson [1](**arrived / came**) ....*arrived*.......... at Grimpen Station by [2](**train / coach**) .... Baskerville Hall is located about half a mile [3](**north / south**) .... of Grimpen Village.

Dr Watson saw a [4](**soldier / policeman**) .... on the road [5](**from / between**) .... Grimpen and Baskerville Hall. The driver said that a [6](**prisoner / big dog**) .... had escaped from Dartmoor Prison.

High Tor is the [7](**highest / lowest**) .... place on the moor. There are [8](**roads / paths**) .... across the moor from Baskerville Hall. Merripit House is [9](**east / west**) .... of High Tor, and High Tor Farm is to the [10](**east / west**) .... – just [11](**north / south**) .... of Coombe Tracey. Lafter Hall is situated roughly [12](**south-east / south-west**) .... of Merripit House.

Making Sentences 1

Put the words in the correct order to make full sentences.

1 BECAUSE HE HAD STOLEN HIS BOOTS SOMEONE
WAS ANGRY.

He was angry because someone had stolen his boots.
....

2 DARTMOOR HAS A PRISON FROM ESCAPED PRISONER.

....

3 BELIEVED SIR HENRY BASKERVILLE HOLMES SOMEONE
TO MURDER THAT WANTED.

....

....

4 BACKWARDS AND FORWARDS THE CANDLE MOVED
BARRYMORE.

....

....

5 ROCKY FROM THE MAN HAD FALLEN THE HILL.

....

6 I AM TO SHOW THE MURDERER WAITING FOR HIMSELF.

....

7 I FIRED THE BLACK SHAPE AT HOLMES AND BOTH
OUR REVOLVERS.

....

8 YOUR COUSIN HAS TAKEN THE GREAT GRIMPEN MIRE.

....

Making Sentences 2

Write questions for the answers.

1 *Who were the Barrymores?*

The Barrymores were servants at Baskerville Hall.

2 *Why*

Stapleton lived on Dartmoor because he was a naturalist.

3 *Where*

The Stapletons lived in Merripit House.

4 *What*

The name of the escaped prisoner was Selden.

5 *Who*

Selden's sister was Mrs Barrymore.

6 *How*

The Barrymores helped Selden by taking him food and clothes.

7 *Who*

Holmes was staying at High Tor Farm.

8 *Who*

Stapleton wanted to kill Sir Henry.

9 *Who*

Holmes, Watson and Inspector Lestrade saved Sir Henry.

10 *What*

Stapleton fell into the Great Grimpen Mire.

Published by Macmillan Heinemann ELT
Between Towns Road, Oxford OX4 3PP
Macmillan Heinemann ELT is an imprint of
Macmillan Publishers Limited
Companies and representatives throughout the world
Heinemann is a registered trademark of Harcourt Education, used under licence.

ISBN 978-0-2300-2924-8
ISBN 978-1-4050-7652-4 (with CD pack)

This retold version by Stephen Colbourn for Macmillan Readers
First published 1992
Text © Stephen Colbourn 1992, 2002, 2005
Design and illustration © Macmillan Publishers Limited 2002, 2005

This edition first published 2005

Illustrated by Kay Dixey
Original cover template design by Jackie Hill
Cover photography by Magnum Photos/Elliott Erwitt

Printed in Thailand
2010 2009 2008
6 5 4 3 2

with CD pack
2010 2009 2008
12 11 10 9 8

Mary, Teach Me to Be Your Daughter

Finding Yourself in the Blessed Mother

MEGAN MADDEN

ASCENSION

West Chester, PA

Ascension
PO Box 1990
West Chester, PA 19380
1-800-376-0520
ascensionpress.com

Cover design: Teresa Ranck

Cover art: *Madonna and Child*, used with permission
        by artist Valerie Delgado (Houston, Texas)

Printed in the United States of America

24 25 26 27 28 6 5 4 3 2

ISBN 978-1-954882-11-9 (paperback)
ISBN 978-1-954882-12-6 (e-book)

Dedicated to Elizabeth Patrice O'Neill

"She is so much like Our Lady;
that is the kind of mother I want to be."

Contents

CHAPTER 1

Mother, Teach Me to Be Your Daughter

Embarking on the Journey

Early in my motherhood, I went on a playdate in the small town where I lived. I was sitting at a round kitchen breakfast table, drinking a cup of coffee and watching my infant crawl across the floor. In the conversation that had been going back and forth between the women, the Blessed Mother was mentioned, and in various comments, I heard an almost exasperated weariness. "Christ was perfect, so Our Lady didn't have to deal with that element of motherhood." "She is the perfect woman, so gentle and meek. I cannot relate to her at all."

I remember sitting in silence wondering if I should say something … but what would I even have to say? Here I am, only nine months into my own motherhood. *What do I even know?* I thought.

The conversation that floated around that little table never left my heart. I brought it into having my next child, my son. I brought it into the unexpectedly fiery temperament of the third child, another sweet little girl. I brought it into the suffering of two successive miscarriages during a time of deep pain, as I underwent that loss, death, and heartbreak. I brought it into the miracle baby that came a year later, and I brought it into my seventh pregnancy, where I brought my fifth child into the world, whose tiny and sweet hands I can still hold today as I write this.

1

One day, I glanced in the mirror and pondered the last several years of my life: the hardships our family had faced, the losses we had experienced, and I began to see my weaknesses in a new way.

I knew I had a devotion to the Blessed Mother. I was born on October 13, the anniversary of the miracle of the sun in Fatima. When I was seven years old, on the day of my first communion, I decided I would dedicate my life to prayer and sacrifice as a Discalced Carmelite nun. In the end, however, this was not to be, as God's plan was that I become a wife and a mother. In my university years, I committed myself to a daily Rosary—something I have not given up since—and I consecrated myself to Our Lady, a consecration that I have renewed diligently, and spoke to her often in prayer. I loved her, certainly, but in this intense moment staring into the mirror as an adult—as a wife and mother now myself who had undergone loss and heartache, who bore countless wounds and remained ever so sinful—I wondered if I even knew Our Lady at all. Did I know the treasures of her heart?

As I thought of Our Lady that day, looking in the mirror, it dawned on me that I had placed her on a pedestal of perfection that was untouchable and that I had no real idea of how to be the intimate daughter of such a radiant and glorious mother. Hidden in my soul was a nagging fear: *Was I good enough to be the daughter of so perfect a mother?*

Perfection

The world demands perfection. It tells us to perfect our bodies according to certain cultural standards of beauty. It tells us to gather material things, accomplishments, achievements, and successes. To "live and let live," yet to never make someone else uncomfortable with the truth (if there even is such a thing). It demands that we show spineless kindness with no regard for what is true, good, and beautiful—that we must pursue self-glorification. It tells us to be greedy and lustful in every way that we can manage.

Heaven, however, has another view of perfection. Heaven tells us to stay lowly, to stay little, to stay impoverished and poor in spirit. It tells us to be detached, to receive the arrows of suffering with peaceful love, to stand courageously in the battle between good and evil, to draw upon the strength of grace met in Jesus Christ in Holy Mother Church and all of the sacraments he has instituted for his beloved little ones. We can follow *the way of littleness* that St. Thérèse of Lisieux taught. There is a bridge to heaven, but it is narrow, for that bridge is the cross and few are willing to make the trek.

Life is filled with hardships, confusion, sins, and doubts. None of us are perfect, and the road we must follow is steep and narrow in its ascent up the high mountain. And yet we are meant to take this hard road while viewing the world through the eyes of eternity. It is precisely in our weakness that our heavenly help desires to come to our aid. It is precisely in our sinfulness that Christ wishes to save us from ourselves. It is precisely in the little, weak, frail, humble way of the saints that the Lord lifts our heads and turns his loving eyes towards us.

We have no need to fear because we are given all that we need when we ask for it; we are given all of the graces necessary for each of our cups—our souls—to be filled with Christ. Each of us has a particular path planned and chosen by God, each is valuable and necessary for the Body of Christ.

Our Lord calls us to "be perfect" (Matthew 5:48), but he does not turn his back on us once he has made this call. He has given us a perfect mother to reach down to us, her beloved children, and help us to rise, to climb, to cling to the cross, to receive the graces her son yearns to pour out on us.

A Perfect Mother for Imperfect Children

God loves his children so much that he has given us this tender woman not only to pray to as our queen—as she who is sinless and contained the uncontainable deserves her queenship—but as our own mother who desires for each of us healing, hope, and joy, who is there for us in all of our sorrows, our loss, and our suffering. I can attest to that. When we call, she is there. When we cry, she consoles. When we are angry, she soothes. When faced with sin and temptation, she helps us to conquer ourselves.

No one is too near or too far not to need Our Lady. What I have learned in prayer and what I offer to you to ponder is this: Rather than compare ourselves to her perfections we might look to her beauty and be inspired by what perfection really is, ready and willing to take the road of the saints.

Our Lady, like her son, did not merely come for the righteous. She is gifted to us as mother precisely because she is a creature, and her heart cannot help but love us deeply, intimately, and truly.

Finding Our Identity in Mary

When I think back to that moment in front of the mirror, I can remember feeling Our Lady so near to me after the questions about my own deficiencies had raced through my mind. I felt the warmth of her maternal heart, received the mantle of her protection, and I said to her in that moment of intimacy, "Mother, teach me to be your daughter."

Welling up within me I had a true sense of my identity in that moment: I am a daughter to the most perfect mother, and I have the most perfect model of motherhood and virtuous womanhood to guide me in my own life, in my motherhood, my femininity, my womanhood, my actions, services, and all my works.

In the year I spent living in Poland, I pondered and mulled over the question of what it meant to be a woman. This question had sprung from my heart as I began to recognize the patterns of a society that raged against the family, against man and woman as God created them, a society that had begun to attempt rewriting the very definition of marriage. This society so steeped in sexual sin, perversion, addiction, and illness was no longer a vague and distant land plagued with rot, but it was one at my doorstep. It was infecting even the most faithful of families, shaking the foundations of traditional family life. I began to identify with the psalmist's cry—"Zeal for your house has consumed me" (Psalm 69:9)—and I thought about what I could do and who I should be in the midst of so much confusion.

Ultimately, I was led down a path that brought me to an undeniably simple answer: a woman is meant to be a mother (be it physically or spiritually). The question went a bit deeper then, as I began to think about its implications. How might I be a true mother, and how might I live out this motherhood in the fullness of my femininity? You may be able to see where I am headed at this point, for Our Lady is the answer. I wished to endeavor to make the journey of becoming a "little mother" in light of Our Lady's perfect example of motherhood, with this littleness rooted in the dignity and beauty of St. Thérèse of Lisieux's Little Way.

Yes, in a world that no longer understands authentic femininity or virtuous womanhood, and which fails to uphold the dignity found in virginity or motherhood, the Blessed Mother proves to be the answer. She is not a woman separated from us in a far and distant land, glancing down from her throne in heaven on rare occasions. Not at all. She is alive—as are all of the saints—and continues to fulfill her mission of eternal motherhood to us. The world needs her motherhood to understand what it means to be a mother.

She knows us deeply and loves us intimately, this woman who is not only the mother of God but the mother of all those bearing the name of Christ in their hearts. In light of Our Lady's motherhood, we might begin to understand her tenderness, her gentleness, her kind spirit, her faithfulness, and her heart's radical, zealous, earnest desire to see her children truly happy and free in the light of her son. And yet the question remains: do we know what it means to be her daughter, and in the light of such a perfect mother is it not fitting to desire to be like her? So we begin, as I once did, with this very simple prayer: "Mother, teach me to be your daughter."

How This Book Works

"Mother, teach me to be your daughter." This prayer is meant to bring healing, grace, and an understanding of just how relational and intimate this book of meditations is meant to be between you and Our Lady, who is full of grace. This simple prayer lies at the core of this book. It is what will thrust each one of us into the discussion of virtue, meditative prayer, and the receptivity that allows for the deepening of our relationship with this perfect, inspiring, and most lovely of all mothers. As you read this book, I encourage you to look back on this prayer, even to write it in a place you will see daily; pray it often, and I promise she will hastily come to your aid.

The saints have assured us continually of our need for Our Lady's intercession in order to enter into the kingdom of heaven. Just as Christ came to the world through Our Lady, so too must we go through her to find him in the fullness of truth. This little book is meant to inspire and foster this devotion to our mother.

It is written for all women, in all states in life, in all circumstances, and all vocations. Whether you are a single woman, or a newlywed hoping for a child, or a mother of children, or a grandmother, or a sister in service or a cloistered nun, you are all called to make the great and lofty pilgrimage to heaven. On this pilgrimage we are called to seek a life of virtue, hope, joy, and freedom from the bondage of sin. We, dear readers, are meant to enter into the depths of family life with God as Father, Christ as brother and bridegroom, and Our Lady as our most holy and venerable queen and mother.

This book is not an academic treatise, nor is it a biblical commentary. I will leave that to the theologians, for whom I have a deep love and respect (my husband, especially, whose theological wisdom helped me with the foundations of this book). This book instead comes from a spirit of prayer and contemplation, from notes I have written down through the years in quiet adoration chapels and from meditative prayer. It came from reading the saints, studying Scripture, and asking questions of those with much more theological knowledge than myself.

This book blossomed in very simple soil, sprung from my heart as a little mother hoping and striving in her own little way for holy womanhood. It is a guide to reflect on Our Lady's principal virtues, in part inspired by the teaching of St. Louis de Montfort who had a great love for Our Lady.

I wrote this book in light of my own spiritual poverty and desire to imitate and ponder Our Lady's virtues along with the guidance of the saints. The ten principal virtues of St. Louis de Montfort, one of the Church's great Marian teachers (and a saint whose wisdom poured forth in love of her), will guide us through this meditative process. He had a deep love of Our Lady and desire to stir devotion to her, as the means to intimacy with Christ. In his books on her perfections, he coined a list of ten principal virtues that Our Lady possessed. He listed them to help us to enter into the mystery of Our Lady's perfections in a practical way, for all of these are virtues we can practice and pray for. In his words,

> True devotion to Our Lady ... leads the soul to avoid sin and to imitate the virtues of the Blessed Virgin, particularly her profound humility, her lively faith, her blind obedience, her continual prayer, her universal mortification, her divine purity, her ardent charity, her heroic patience, her angelic sweetness and her divine wisdom. These are the ten principal virtues of the most holy Virgin.[1]

Beside each virtue St. Louis de Montfort defined as intrinsic to our Lady's person, I have placed an additional virtue that can assist us in practical imitation, specifically as women striving for sanctity.

I hope it is an opportunity to meditate on her life, on her hiddenness, her strength, and her queenship. This ultimately pushes us to discover her in the midst of our own life story, to discover who she is and what she means for us and, even more, who we are to her. The best way to read this book is with a disposition of spiritual poverty and receptivity, placing ourselves near to our mother and hearing her speak to our hearts.

Setting Out

To begin this journey of meditating on the virtues of Our Lady, I think it is important to take the time to reflect on a few questions. What areas in my life need healing? What does holy motherhood—be it in women surrounding me or my own experience—mean to me? What is God asking of me in this current season of my life? How can I embrace my identity as a woman? How can I fully embrace my femininity and my maternal qualities? And finally: what prayers might I commit to every day in order to better honor, love, and know our Blessed Mother? There is no one too far or too near that does not need her guiding hand to make progress in the spiritual ascent to holiness.

Heaven tells us to climb the mountain, to gain mastery over our passions, to strive with perseverance and strength. When we fall heaven calls out to us and demands, "Rise up, again, my daughter!" Again, and again, and again. Our Lady's motherhood and queenship is something that should inspire us rather than intimidate us. As our Mother, she hopes to teach us holy womanhood, holy maidenhood, and holy motherhood. She is a faithful companion and guiding hand who is able to offer us strength and wisdom as she intercedes for us on our journey to God.

I hope that in pondering the life of Our Lady—veiled in so many ways and hidden in so much mystery and beauty—that we can begin to understand more fully the dignity of authentic femininity, virtuous womanhood, and our call to be a "little mother" in imitation of our mother in heaven. In this rootedness and self-knowledge, I hope we each become ever more humbled as we face the perfection Our Lady embodies, and that we choose to become like her simply by loving her.

"MOTHER, TEACH ME TO BE YOUR DAUGHTER."

CHAPTER 2

Fiat in Each Moment

Imitating Mary's Humility as a Receptive Woman

When the angel Gabriel arrived in the little house of Nazareth—the humble home where the little maiden lived and stayed and served and rested—he found her as one might expect to find the future Mother of God: in a state of humble prayer, with an empty heart ready to receive Jesus. And yet, though this is what one might expect, there is a mystery here. How could Mary's heart—that heart full of grace—be called "empty"? At the same time, how could she receive God's gift if her heart was not empty? Meditating on this mystery will reveal a deep truth about our own readiness to receive God's gifts.

Prepared to Receive

Even though this young girl was perfectly sinless, she was not immune to the fallen world. She suffered and felt deeply the mountains and valleys of life. She felt sorrow, loneliness, and the spiritual emptiness all of us feel at one point or another. It is an emptiness we very often feel before receiving a great gift from God. As the great spiritual doctors St. John of the Cross and St. Teresa of Avila note, in the spiritual life, there comes a stripping, an emptying prior to union. This is a humbling process that is usually felt distinctly as darkness and abandonment. Since she was conceived without sin, Mary experienced a spiritual union with God from the beginning and always—and was therefore unable to lose his sight and grace. Yet she was also made ready and prepared to receive him in time and in space.

Her state of spiritual poverty and emptiness provided the readiness necessary to receive the great gift of God's Son. This gift is incommunicable, and it is the greatest gift ever to be received by woman: She was to become the mother of God.

MARY'S HUMILITY AND RECEPTIVITY

The Son of God came to a little girl, in a small village, who though perfect, lived a quiet and quite ordinary daily life. She was a little girl willing to serve, a little girl who loved to love, a little girl with an open heart and a great love of God, ready to give of herself in any way she could in order to give God glory and love her neighbor as herself. Her humility radiated as light and inspired those around her to check their pride at the door, to be a little more like the humble, prayerful, unique daughter of Anne and Joachim.

Those who knew her must have noticed she was unique. Her parents were quite aware of the gift she was to them and in raising her could see her perfections, prayer, and holiness. No mother or father could be unaware of such qualities. Neighbors and friends must have seen these things in her as well—her kindness and her humility surpassing that of anyone they had ever met.

And yet, in spite of her unique gifts, there were traits that prepared her heart that are in fact relatable to all women. A humble disposition is one of them, for that is the foundation of any man or woman's spiritual life. Very particularly, her deep humility led to a profound receptivity, a quality of the feminine genius that all women possess.

Since Mary was perfectly humble, she did not need any purgation as we do in preparation to receive Christ. She did however experience the gift of Christ and the loss of Christ physically a number of times in her earthy life. This loss did not come from sin, of course, but she experienced it in the most tangible ways. She lost him in Jerusalem when he was twelve years old, and she lost him on the cross for three more dark days in his adult life. Knowing that she too experienced this emptiness ignites in us a deeper understanding of her Immaculate Heart, a heart which imitates and takes on her son's penitent and very real suffering. Her heart is a heart that we might relate to in our daily crosses and spiritual dark nights, as well as spiritual poverty.

Mary had a deep understanding both of the dark night of the soul and of the feeling of a quiet and hidden God. Because she knew this well, she reasoned from a young age that she was a lowly maiden, and her God is he who Is. The fruit of this humble disposition, of knowing her nothingness compared to God's vastness and almighty glory, was a spiritual emptiness that prepared her heart for the great gift to come. Though humiliations are nothing short of unpleasant to experience, the result for all of us on the ascent to holiness is what Mary rightly had: an understanding of the lowliness of creatures before God.

Our Lady out of all human beings knew and felt this most intensely. She experienced the natural ebb and flow of the spiritual life. The feelings of desolation and consolation were even intensified due to her perfections. Her heart felt these things acutely since her capacity for love was so great, due to her lack of sinfulness.

And so, on that shining day in Nazareth when the Word became Incarnate, she received the Son of God and the greatest consolation a human being had ever received. She received him not with haughty pride, but with her head bowed low. Her lowliness attracted God even more to her vast soul with a great and perfect capacity to love. At once the Holy Spirit fell upon her and overshadowed her, and God became Man. The One who could never be contained in time and space chose from the foundation of the world to be contained in this little maiden's empty womb and spiritually in her heart.

THE JOY OF HUMILITY

In this little hovel in Nazareth, the impossible became possible since God willed it to be so. As a burst from her heart to her cousin Elizabeth, she exclaimed that "he has regarded the low estate of his handmaiden"

(Luke 1:48). She knew she was blessed, and she received God's gift with a great joy and deep residing happiness. The moment of her *fiat* was a moment in salvation history that affected the entire cosmos, and yet it happened not in a parade before others, not to an earthly queen who was admired and widely known, not in a palace, not with a crowd, not to anyone seemingly important. St. Ignatius of Antioch expands on this saying, "Now the virginity of Mary was hidden from the prince of this world, as was also her offspring, and the death of the Lord; three mysteries of renown, which were wrought in silence by God."[2] God chose a hidden, humble rooftop under which to live. He chose poverty from the start; tangible poverty and a little girl with a heart that embraced spiritual poverty. Our Lady was all he wanted in a mother, everything he meant and desired a woman, a maiden, a bride, a mother to be—why wouldn't she be, she was his design! And so that quiet noontime visit from the angel changed everything, and suddenly she had become the mother of God; her life had changed forevermore.

After the fact, in her exclamation of joy to her cousin Elizabeth, not only does she recount her humility and lowliness, but she simultaneously says that "all generations will call me blessed" (Luke 1:48). Humility is so often thought to mean a meekness that is self-deprecating. But in fact, it is to know who one is and who one is not. If one is a queen, it would not be humble for her to act as if she were not a queen. If one is a servant, it would not be humble for her to act as if she were not a servant. Mary was both. She understood she was a creature and that she was a humble handmaiden and, simultaneously, she knew it was a gift and privilege to be the Mother of God, that she was made on this earth to fulfill this call and mission.

She embraced earthly poverty with a holy confidence and was receptive to the unexpected, to a God who would ask to come to a hidden place and live a hidden quiet life until the appointed time, served primarily by her in their very ordinary home. She swept the floors and washed the dishes; she baked his bread and mended his clothes. All things were done in the most ordinary of ways with extraordinary love. And while she knew how unusual the situation was, she did not make an attempt to rewrite God's story to make it grander and fitting for a king. She was the humble servant, the maiden, and her lowliness brought her to great glory, which was fully recognized only in her death and Assumption, her crowning in the next life.

Mary's *fiat* was all-encompassing, she accepted and received Christ's whole life in one moment within her blessed womb. She said yes to Christ's birth, Christ's childhood, Christ's priesthood, Christ's ministry, Christ's death, and Christ's resurrection. Her yes resounded in every moment of Christ's earthly life and thereafter. She accepted and received all God planned for her and her son.

She knew after her *fiat* that all generations would call her blessed. She was not looking to herself and her own glory, but she knew she would be called blessed precisely because she was considered worthy to receive and bear the Son of God and forever carry this timeless weight. But just as an earthly queen carries the weight of the jewels in her crown, the Mother of God carried the weight of the jewels in the heavenly crown that was to be hers. This was a weight of sacrifice and suffering that she embraced wholeheartedly.

Her deep humility is explicitly shown in her acceptance of both joy and sorrow, misunderstandings, troubles, and trials. When Joseph was troubled, she reacted in humble silence, quite contrary to human nature. When Herod pursued the death of the Christ Child, she obeyed her husband's promptings and fled to a foreign land without question. She was always in a state of deep humility and receptivity to God's holy and divine will. Because of this, she knew more than anyone how to receive all gifts: with great and abundant joy.

How Might We Grow in Receptivity?

A woman's nature is receptive. Receptivity is a natural part of woman that is clearly shown in her physical makeup. It is a gift made tangible in her ability to receive the seed of new life within her body. Unlike for a man, this act of union can have a result that is extended further than just the moment of conception; the woman holds a new life within her body for nine months and during that time nourishes, protects, and fosters this life within her. In this act of union, the woman receives the gift of her husband's loving friendship and primarily, when God so wills it, receives the gift of a child. When this life is fostered and formed within her, there is a mysterious act of God by which he infuses a new soul within this new body, fashioned and growing within the womb.

In all of these circumstances, there is a physical reception of spousal love that forms the body of the unborn child, and there is a mysterious spiritual reception of a new soul, united to this new little body, that is given as gift by God alone. It is the privilege of woman to hold this new immortal life within her, to foster, nourish, and bear that life into the external world.

RECEIVING THE HEART

Beyond this obvious and physical form of receptivity, the natural receptivity of a woman runs even deeper than this. There is a spiritual and emotional element of her receptivity. It is evident that a woman naturally desires to receive another's heart and to nourish and care for the souls of family, friends, loved ones, and anyone given in relationship to her.

The beauty of the Blessed Mother and her own receptivity is that she can relate to all women in all states of life. She relates to the maiden as virgin, to the wife as bride, to the mother who brings forth a physical child, and to the spiritual mother who wisely guides her spiritual children through the perils of life. In whatever ways the receptivity of woman is made manifest, a woman can find comfort in Our Lady's example as the physical mother of Christ and the spiritual mother of all the faithful. In every case, she can relate to the ability and desire to conceive and receive Christ within the depths of her heart.

THREE STEPS TO RECEPTIVITY

But what does it mean to possess a holy and perfected receptivity? How might one tap into the gift of receptivity more fully and grow in it? Turning to the mother of God we see three main steps to achieving this holy reception: she is first humble and made empty, next she receives what is given as gift, and then she rejoices.

Before we look at each part there is a point to make here: if we are hoping to purify this characteristic of receptivity in ourselves, we cannot move straightaway to pure joy before we are emptied, and we cannot fully receive before we are made humble. Because of our fallen nature, a process of purgation is necessary, and this often feels uncomfortable. It is meant to stretch us and help us see the world and our life from the perspective of God's heavenly plan. He will enlighten, illumine, and guide along the way, most especially giving graces through prayers and the sacraments. The greatest saints received the greatest gifts due to their foundation in humility and in the knowledge of their nothingness before God. Our Lady, having received the most precious gift of all women, can be our guiding hand up the mountaintop where we will rejoice and be glad. This leads us to the foundational characteristic for this ascent: humility.

1. Humble and Emptied

As we have seen, Our Lady receives the Son of God not with pride but with her head bowed low. We too are meant to receive her son fully into our hearts and to know and hear his voice acutely. How do we become humble? Humility is acquired (in short) by prayers such as the Litany of Humility, asking God to make us humble, and by undergoing various humiliations as a way to practice.

A woman working on the foundation of humility might look to Our Lady's silence at Joseph's confusion and astonishment when he learned of her pregnancy. There are certainly times to speak, just as there are also times to be silent. Mary knew she was meant to be silent even though this was a significant humiliation. The humble woman will fight her pride with silence when words bring division, rotten fruit, damage to others' well-being, and when they are the product of gossip or detraction of any kind.

The woman seeking humility will also accept various mis-understandings as little pinches forming her character, and when those pinches hurt, she will bring them to God and ask for his consoling hand and unwavering peace to fill her. Silence in the wake of misunderstandings, or in desiring to over-explain oneself, is a tangible way to root out pride, and it can be practiced all too often.

Humility is not an easy virtue to cultivate, but over time the purgative process—with the assistance of God's grace—strips the self of pride more thoroughly, including all natural attachments to being well-regarded, or of being popular, or of putting an inordinate weight in the opinion of others. These things can be healed in Christ and washed away with the freedom found in humility. And this emptying results in an intense longing for her heart to be filled; she desires God alone and seeks in earnest the heavenly kingdom as her true home. This longing takes the place of the material and creature comforts she once sought, and the weight of praise and blame of others that once held such strongholds on her heart.

As soon as God sees the open door of the heart, he longs, he aches, he yearns to bring his gifts—most significantly to enter into the heart of woman and reside within her heart always, as a quiet little sanctuary emptied precisely for his presence and light to fill. This reception is often first placed as a seed which then continues to grow.

2. Receiving God's Gifts

At this point self-knowledge begins to flourish, and the woman knows who she is as creature before the God who loves her ever so much. And a woman becomes who she is meant to be, by and through the fruit of Christ living within her. Because she was previously emptied, there is room for him inside her heart to rest comfortably; her heart expands.

This reception might come as a little light day by day as she frees up the space of her heart to receive God. Or it might come in a swift moment of sweet consolation in intimate prayer. Or, as is often the case, it might feel messy, imperfect, and be a daily battle and struggle to overcome herself and struggle to grow. But she will begin to bloom over the course of time. In any circumstance, the more emptied she is, the more she is able to receive, and in this reception, she will be made joyful and enter into an authentic state of peace with a cheerful heart.

3. Rejoicing in the Gift

Our Lady shows us the proper reaction to receiving any little or great gift from God. Perhaps that gift is a small spiritual consolation, or perhaps it is his resounding presence in our lives. Perhaps it is the little good thing that happened that morning: a baby sleeping through the night or a kind word from a stranger, a promotion at work, or a prospect of marriage. It is fitting for a woman especially, after receiving any gift, to rejoice in it, trusting all it entails with all its weight to God as Our Lady received the Christ Child with all that his coming entailed and all the weight of sacrifice and suffering to come.

It may sound easy to us, in theory, to rejoice in the gift, but there are so many circumstances where we receive gifts from God and struggle to rejoice in them. Perhaps we are overwhelmed with worry: If I take on this new promotion at work, it will require more hours. I did not plan on another pregnancy so quickly; will it be too hard? I'm not sure I am ready to get married but now this wonderful man has walked into my life, and I would love to spend my life with him! You see there are so many circumstances where

God desires to give us gifts that, though they make us happy, bring a weight of responsibility we may feel hesitant to take on.

But love always comes with responsibility. Love always comes with sacrifice, and though it is against our fallen human nature to want anything to be trying or difficult, the great things we receive in life will always come with a portion of suffering and sacrifice. The servant will be called to imitate her master, to be like Jesus.

When Our Lady ran to Elizabeth in the hill country, she proclaimed everything with a wondrous joy and happiness. She laughed with her dear cousin and friend as women who speak with the words of the Spirit laugh in great and utter joy—uplifting their minds and hearts to God. This did not detract from her suffering, but it brought about a true and authentic joy. She shows each of us how to accept the weight of *our jewels* in each of our crowns waiting for us in the heavenly courts. Though worry may creep in, it is Mary who can teach us to receive the happiness and joy that comes when something exciting in life takes place.

Whether it be receiving a meal from a friend on a difficult day of mothering, exclaiming over a thoughtful birthday gift, listening to a family member or friend in need, receiving a guest into your home for dinner, or even receiving a consolation from God, let us practice being women of reception. Let us allow this natural disposition to grow within us. It may be a little seedling at first with perhaps very little room to grow in the space of our hearts. However, when we weed out our attachments, watering our souls with humility and asking Christ to dwell within us as the sun, we can create a magnificent garden in our souls for the Lord to dwell and take rest.

We, like Our Lady, can give our *fiat* and receive God and all of his gifts both directly from him and through the love of others without fear and without worry but with authentic rejoicing. "Sing aloud, O daughter of Zion; shout, O Israel! Rejoice and exult with all your heart, O daughter of Jerusalem!" (Zephaniah 3:14).

The Hidden One
Imitating Mary's Lively Faith as a Maternal Woman

The birth of our Lord was and always will be a mystery on earth, a mystery that shook the cosmos, a mystery that began in a tangible way in Bethlehem when she held the Christ Child and kissed his face for the very first time. She locked eyes with that precious babe the moment he was born, she nursed him, she warmed him, she clothed him, she soothed him. He looked helpless and weak in her arms, and she pondered ... he chose to *need her*. The Son of God chose her to be his mother.

Mary's call to motherhood was supernatural, laid upon the foundation of her faith. For every woman, a call to motherhood stirs in her heart, and that call bears fruit when she, too, receives it with faith. It is in the heart of Our Lady's example that a woman will find the answer to what she is meant to be to her children—the physical children born of her body, or the spiritual children nurtured in her heart.

Mary's Motherhood

The Divine had touched the heart of this mother from the beginning, and so the Divine continued to live within her. But now God dwelt outside her, too. God's presence dwelt in her heart and in the reality of the son before her.

MOTHER OF GOD

No one who knew her could deny her peace, no one felt unloved or uncared for in her presence. All those who approached her went away with the joy that only comes when met with kindness, truth, and compassion. All who approach her even now find the same compassion that she showed during her days on earth.

Her radiance stemmed from her interior life and union with God, an unwavering and lively faith in him and his promises from the beginning. Prior to the Annunciation, the seed of faith already had grown within this holy mother's heart; it blossomed into her faith in the words of the angel. Having memorized the sacred writings of the law, being steeped in the Psalms (the breviary of ancient Israel), and all of the promises of Scripture, she was aware when the angel came that she was the woman chosen to bear the Messiah. There is even a pious tradition that holds that it was while she was reading the Psalms that the angel Gabriel appeared to her. This initial meeting and act of faith in what was to come enacted and brought forth her motherhood.

Her motherhood was the foundation of who she was even before the conception of Christ. Her soul and body had been touched by the Divine from her own conception, keeping her free from sin in anticipation of the *fiat* that would pave the way for human redemption. Her part was not as a peg used by God for a particular outcome. Her part was to exist as a woman fashioned by the greatest love of God, as the most perfect creature—the masterpiece of humankind. She was created with the grace to become the New Eve, the new mother of the living.

When Gabriel told her she would have a child, her response of "How could this be?" was not in the spirit of a lack of faith in God's abilities, but instead a revelation of her promise of perpetual virginity. Was God asking her to break this promise? She was perplexed as she knelt before the angel and asked for clarity on the matter. The Spirit came upon her, and the Son of God took on her flesh, her blood, and chose to be nourished in his own body by her own body. She was pregnant with the author of all life. This pregnancy led to the quiet of a night when a newborn babe was born into the world under the humblest of roofs, with the only visible splendor that of the shining star overhead. As Our Lady gave birth her body was kept intact, revealing the sacredness of her virginity and protecting the initial promise she was deeply concerned to keep.

The becoming that happens when a mother meets her child for the first time took place in the quiet of a very dark night, with a certain star hovering in the heavens above, leading a select few to the hidden scene. With Jesus knelt the woman of faith who held him tightly in her arms, head bent downward and eyes radiating a deep confidence in the God who can do all things. Her face shone with innocence, beauty, goodness, and truth. The maiden was a mother and yet retained her maidenhood. Mary saw herself as she was in light of God's image: she was the *Theotokos*, the Mother of God, and generation after generation would call her blessed. She was the Virgin *Theotokos*, taking up all aspects of womanhood.

THE STRENGTH OF FAITH

When Mary held Jesus as a little baby, *her* little baby, she knew he was the Son of God—she had been set upon a mission fraught with danger, public appearances, spiritual battles, and ministry. From the beginning, Our Lady embraced God's will in the depths of her heart. Her *fiat* radiated in the continual choice to serve her Lord and her neighbor with love and diligence, and it is her faith which brought her the gift of courage to bear all things, no matter how extraordinary and strange to the world around her.

The Christ Child grew and was wise beyond his years. She pondered the great mystery of motherhood in her heart and what was to come of this son whom she called her own, whom her husband protected as though his own flesh and blood.

It is faith that brought her strength. It is faith that brought her trust. It is faith that ignited hope in even the most dreadful of her life's dark moments: when the Son of God lay dead in her arms.

Her faith never shook, it never faltered, and it never left her, because she was a woman full of grace without stain, sin, or imperfections. The drama of the cross is the climax of her faith. But looking at her life as a whole is a reminder to us that to be entrusted with significant missions, we must first remain faithful in the small things.

When she was pregnant, would St. Joseph leave her side? Would she be abandoned by society and viewed as an adulteress? When Simeon said her heart would be pierced, would she be struck with fear and anxiety? When Christ began his public ministry, would she lose her son?

If she was labeled an adulterer for the sake of the Savior's birth, so be it. If she was to suffer for the sake of humanity, she would do it. If her son must die, she would resign herself to his will. She did what any good mother would do. She refused to turn in on herself for the good of her child, for the good of all those who would be her spiritual sons and daughters in the Lord; she poured herself forth out of a heart of love through active service.

HIDDEN PEACE

It is precisely the hiddenness of the early days of Our Lady's motherhood that sheds light on the sacredness of this precious and quiet time with her son. That hiddenness was so significant that the world knows very little about the early days in Nazareth. Those moments are wrapped into Our Lady's mantle which hides away the precious time of union and physical closeness between her and her son. Sacred art and tradition depict these days of Our Lady's motherhood as an embrace between her and her son, as a "kiss" of union between the two, a deep intimacy of relationship in their shared will.

Those days were filled with peace and authentic happiness. In those quiet and unseen hours, the homemaker's work was elevated in dignity, as Our Lady served in the same tasks. Our Lady's mind, unclouded by sin or ignorance, expressed itself in an ordered and simple home; her prayer manifesting in service, her wisdom in thoughtful decision making, her prudence in purchases for the good of her family, her quiet heart leading to a peaceful way about her.

She was a simple woman, with a simple home. She swept the kitchen floor, and her sweeping was done as present service. She cooked meals and baked bread with care and joy. She patiently put the child Jesus to sleep, watching him breathe and slip into dreamland in the most ordinary of ways. The simple home in Nazareth was peaceful, and the essence of the Divine dwelled therein because perfections dwelled within.

It could have shined bright, it could have drawn people in from all districts to see the perfect child, the appointed one who had come. But word did not carry through the districts. Not yet. Mary kept his secret, speaking only of these mysteries when necessary and with the right persons. She carried and cared for the light of the world, and she herself, the little mother, would one day be crowned Queen of Heaven and Earth and Mother of all of the living. She rested silently in the ordinary, patiently and joyfully raising him with an outpouring of love to which every mother can relate, but which no mother can fully comprehend.

She looked into the eyes of her son and saw his love for humanity, his love for her having already saved her and kept her clean from even the stain of original sin. God had touched her humanity and filled her with grace. Her faith welled up as life-giving water, rushing forth from her heart and into the mundane day-to-day moments, elevating them and making them holy. She would know the God-Man intimately and more perfectly than any creature ever did or ever would.

During these days of love between the Holy Family, Christ lived a simple life of trade and study and bore all parts of humanity patiently. The

Blessed Mother kept him safe and hidden from public ministry within the quiet home of Nazareth with family and friends until the appointed hour. Her lively faith shines brightly in these quiet moments, just as much (if not more) than the most dramatic moments in the life of Christ.

The quiet days in Nazareth were met with laughter, feasts, fasts, learning, trade, and work. There was a steady normalcy in these acts, and yet they were taken on by the loveliest of persons, with the most perfect of virtues. Our Lady was the woman of Proverbs 31 in the flesh, the woman in Scripture known for her wisdom and faithfulness to her duties, filled with purpose and joy in her daily tasks of caring for house and home. The only difference between Our Lady and all other women, the only separation we have from this transcendent perfection of the duty of the moment, is our sin.

How Might We Grow in Our Maternal Nature with the Foundation of a Lively Faith?

The Blessed Mother's faith was foundational to her *fiat* and to the entirety of her mission. Without faith, there are certainly good deeds that can be done, but they lack the depth and significance of a life given to God and proclaiming God. A woman's natural call to motherhood is sanctified in faith.

RECEIVING THE GIFT OF FAITH WITH PRAYER

Faith is an interesting virtue because no one can cultivate it by habit; it is pure gift. With receptivity as an intrinsic feminine quality, a woman is uniquely ready to receive the gift of faith, a gift that is given directly from God by grace and by means of the sacraments.

Faith is aroused first and foremost by a growing prayer life and dedication to the holy sacraments of the Church. In all states of a woman's life, prayer is meant to be cultivated with a deep reverence and faithful dedication. Some seasons make a developed prayer life overwhelming. For instance, a postpartum mother may feel overstretched, exhausted in the early days of motherhood and caring for a newborn. A working woman may feel she has no time in her mornings and evenings to set aside with all of her responsibilities. An older woman may feel a certain weariness and desire for refreshment in the spirit of joy and renewed energy. A cloistered nun or teaching sister may feel her prayer becoming repetitive and dry, and she may find that when there is an allotted time for prayer, her mind begins to wander. And yet these moments of weakness, frailty, and evident imperfection are precisely what attracts Christ to his lowly ones.

The woman of faith knows a little secret about dark days and desert nights in prayer: the secret of seasons and the process of the spiritual life. The saints teach that it is precisely in these seasons—when not ignited by our own sin and choice to create distance—that spiritual progress and intimacy with Christ takes place. It is in feeling nothing and yet believing without that feeling. It is in praying prayers out of duty, even when it is in the spirit of obedience. It is in beginning new each day despite feeling that God is so very far away. When prayers are said in any of these states, they are some of the most powerful and purifying prayers of all.

The key is to stay dedicated and dutiful during times of dryness, picking selective prayers and times to say them. Then throughout the day, small prayers can be managed—for instance, saying grace before meals, praying the angelus at noon, a litany during morning or evening prayer. The single woman in particular has an opportunity to develop a disciplined prayer life with set times and hours. A mother of children may have time slots planned, but she will need to allow these times to be flexible and to embrace her children's interruptions as part of her prayer. These interruptions are, in fact, a part of her call to a particular patience and discipline. The religious sister may diligently bring her mind and heart to the present moment and choose spiritual reading which ignites her love of God and refreshes her in her vocation.

The Rosary, in particular, is the most powerful prayer outside of Holy Mass and is met with the promise of many graces and perfections at the hands of Our Lady. In all seasons and in all cases, a fervent prayer life is the foundation to receiving and deepening the intensity of the gift of faith, which the woman of prayer must ask for. Asking for faith is a prayer that will never be denied by the Lord and will be foundational to a woman's active service, just as it was foundational to Our Lady's service in Nazareth.

THE FREEDOM TO BE A MOTHER

With faith comes self-knowledge, and in a woman's reflection of self, she discovers the gifts of her femininity, grounding herself in her natural maternal instinct. All women are called to be mothers, be it spiritual or physical. It is intrinsically linked to the psychological makeup of the feminine existence to possess deep within the recesses of her heart a variety of maternal qualities: gentleness, kindness, compassion, wisdom, counsel, protectiveness, purity, and loveliness.

Sometimes it is difficult to tap into these qualities because of the wounds we have suffered and the healing we might still need. In light of this, we might consider our own wounds. What feminine gifts make us uncomfortable, and why might that be? How does God wish to reach this part of our hearts and heal a foundational part of our identity: womanhood? In the modern world, women are particularly attacked and often wounded in the area of motherhood. It is the battle against motherhood, a battle against marriage and family. This becomes obvious when we look at the onslaught of abortion, the widespread use of contraception, and the explosion of pornography, scandalous dress, and sexual objectification, which strip away female dignity.

The first step to break woman down in this manner is to strip her of her natural instincts as mother; in taking down a mother, one certainly takes down the family. The strange thing about this mindset is that it demands that a woman reject her maternal qualities to achieve true freedom and happiness. This is where Our Lady steps in and paves the way for all women, showing the dignity and privilege of authentic femininity and virtuous womanhood.

In meeting her, we are healed, as she is not a mother who brings harsh judgment on her daughters. This would not be fruitful for the mission she maintains in heaven. Instead, she is the mother who wants to heal all of her sons and daughters on earth by drawing all men and women to Christ. She meets us with tender, maternal care, and we have an opportunity to respond. We have an opportunity to receive her motherhood more fully: "Mother, teach me to be your daughter." It is significant that the foundation of what we ask for, as women, is healing in the areas of our maternal nature and instinct. We ask to be able to see and possess fully our gifts so that we might live them out in a true sense of self-knowledge as women and in freedom.

MOTHERHOOD FOR EVERY WOMAN

These expressions of our womanhood will be lived out externally in a number of different ways in each state of life. Whether physical or spiritual, motherhood calls to every woman. With Our Lady's faithful maternity as her guide, the single woman, the vowed religious woman, and the married woman find their mission as mothers.

The single woman is meant to express her maternal qualities through acts of service and her work in society. To those around her, she gives her very best when she identifies herself in the eyes of a Father who loves her. In all her work and service, she brings along her femininity, her particular complementary gifts. Her maternal nature brings a different perspective in the areas of science, engineering, business, accounting, the arts, teaching, and humanities. Certainly, there are more notably feminine jobs than others, but overall, there is simply no work into which a woman cannot pour her maternal instinct. If she is called to do it by God, she can pour her feminine qualities, especially her motherhood, into that work. It is through this sense of identity that she will be successful in her mission.

The bride—be it the spiritual bride of Christ or the earthly sacramental bride—will similarly pour herself into her work and service of those around her. The spiritual bride of Christ, the vowed religious, has a particularly unique role by surpassing what is natural and entering into a spiritual marriage. This marriage is called to bear the fruit of many children. The spiritual bride of Christ may know her spiritual children personally, helping and guiding them along their way, or she may be praying for souls completely unknown to her across the world but tied to her in prayer. She becomes a spiritual mother of many sons and daughters in close imitation of the Blessed Mother, who takes all of us under her mantle.

The married woman enters into a sacramental union in holy matrimony, and through that union, there is an intensifying of her role as it begins to take shape in light of vocation. In meeting her husband, she sees the differences between man and woman acutely. She is successful in her role as wife if she sees these complementary qualities as gifts to further ignite her friendship with her spouse.

In the case of an earthly bride's infertility, the heavy cross she bears may lead her to spiritual motherhood. Our Lady assists and comforts because her own spiritual motherhood to all of us proves that spiritual motherhood is profound, deep, and real. The spiritual mother cares for her many spiritual children in her state, work, and service that she is called to do. There is always work to be done, people to love, community to build, and the dedicated spiritual mother will find those opportunities. She will use them as a means to further hospitality and expand the warmness of her heart to those around her. She is called to find and live out this spiritual motherhood.

Then there is the most tangible state, natural motherhood, and it is the earthly mother whose call outside of herself lays before her in the form of a new human being. She may have one child or a large family, and it is only in the heart of Our Lady's example that she will find the answer to what she is meant to be to her children. It is a call outside of herself, beginning with the gift of her body to her husband and then the gift of her body to her child. She will bloom with life for nine months before giving birth, she will experience the postpartum period, and she will note the changes in her body. She will experience sleepless nights, busy days where she seems to get nothing at all done, and moments where she feels utterly depleted of self.

For every mother, spiritual or physical, her primary call is to help her children become saints and guide them along life's journey, being a safe haven and nurturing spirit, hiding them from the evils of the world until the appointed time, sheltering them in the peace of a loving home, and diligently teaching them the ways of God.

The maternal nature of woman matures and becomes fully clear in light of her faith. Why? Because just as our Lady gave birth to faith spiritually by and through her *fiat*, all women are meant to nourish their own faith within. This, in turn, will pour forth into their womanhood, and into their motherhood.

"Behold, a virgin shall conceive and bear a son, and his name shall be called Emmanuel" (Matthew 1:23).

CHAPTER 4

Wisdom Poured Forth

Imitating Mary's Obedience
as a Discerning Woman

The hill country stirred as the wise men related what they had seen of the star: the king of the Jews was born, and they had come to meet and worship him. Herod, upon hearing this, was troubled and sent a decree to destroy the little ones two years and under for the sake of his kingship. News spread fast, village upon village aroused by what was coming and anxious over how to protect their little ones. Upon receiving this news, Our Lady was troubled. She assuredly turned to prayer and looked upon her husband, who was given to her as a gift, always to protect her and the little baby she held in her arms. One moment they were welcoming a newborn baby in the humble confines of a manger, and the next, they were fleeing the country to save the life of this mysterious little king.

Even though it was the wise men who told Herod of Christ, it was God's plan, and it was significant that they met the child and came to worship him before his departure. These men of the East came with wisdom and met the woman so often depicted as "Wisdom" herself. And so, when danger was near, and St. Joseph was warned in a dream to flee, Mary responded with wise discernment, obeying God and the husband he gave her to lead her. She sanctified not only that great moment of danger but the small moments of poverty that followed, moments we all experience in some way, by embracing the unknown with obedience and trust in the Lord. It is through discernment and obedience that we, too, may become women of virtue, women with wisdom to share with our children.

Mary's Obedience in the Darkness

In the dark of the night, while Our Lady rested close to the Christ Child, St. Joseph had a dream. He quickly awoke and, with haste, said they must flee. He recounted all that he heard, and Our Lady listened. Without question, they gathered their belongings and prepared for their journey in the night.

"Rise, take the child and his mother, and flee to Egypt, and remain there till I tell you; for Herod is about to search for the child, to destroy him" (Matthew 2:13). St. Joseph and Our Lady were not prepared to leave their family and loved ones, they were not prepared to travel to the unknown land of their ancestors, they were not prepared to be aliens in a foreign country. They were unready in every way, and yet they knew they must be obedient to the promptings in this dream. When St. Joseph relayed this dream to the Blessed Mother, she did not question his instinct and leadership. She knew he was just, faithful, and discerning; that she could rely on God's protection by way of her husband. Without being aware of the outcome and without knowing any details, she obeyed her husband's promptings and followed him into the unknown.

She bore the baby Jesus on a dark night and traveled to Egypt under the cover and protection of yet another night. In this, we might see the spiritual side of what was tangibly happening. The heart of Our Lady knew darkness well. She knew what it was like to feel as if God was far away even though he was intimately close.

Spiritually, Our Lady's heart felt this darkness even when Christ was closer to her than ever before, not only in her blessed womb but now in her arms where she could see him with her eyes, hear him with her ears, kiss his face, hold his hands, and care for our God incarnate. Her maternal heart ached thinking of leaving her family and relations behind her for an unknown amount of time. Most of all, her maternal heart ached knowing her child was in serious danger of death almost immediately after he was born; all was dark in this humble woman, this little mother's heart as she prepared to flee under the protection and vulnerability of the present darkness.

DISCERNMENT

What would this child be? Even though many of the Jewish people thought the Messiah would come as a political leader and magnificent king that would conquer lands and lead great battles for freedom and prosperity, in her depths from the very beginning, his mother knew he was destined to die. Because she was the woman of wisdom, her understanding of the Psalms surpassed all scholars of her time and thereafter, as she remembered, "Yes, I hear the whispering of many— terror on every side!—as they scheme together against me, as they plot to take my life" (Psalm 31:13). Was this the fulfillment of that passage, would he die as quickly as he came? It was not. For in St. Joseph, she knew she would find protection and in her prompt obedience to his assertion that they should, in fact, leave their land for a foreign nation she found a resounding and unshakable peace within the turmoil.

Our Lady's obedience demonstrates her ability to discern the truth of things. The star of the East paved the way for this intimate meeting where they fell down, prostrated before him, and worshiped the Christ Child, giving him gifts of gold, frankincense, and myrrh; gifts which Our Lady received knowing the poetic and prophetic meaning behind each. She understood the symbolism of her child as priest, prophet, and king. She had eyes to see and the ability to understand what is true.

TRUST

She knew her baby, the God-Man, was protected and that St. Joseph's dream had saved his life. She knew and trusted in every prompting of her husband's voice, for he was a virtuous man, and as her husband would never ask her to do anything contrary to the will of God. Despite the painstaking aspects of the situation, she acted as a woman of wisdom who knew God had a plan, and that her husband was the leader of their holy family, even though she could not see what was ahead of her or the answers to all of the imminent questions.

She recalled, "Out of Egypt I called my son" (Hosea 11:1), but there were many things she did not know. How long they would reside in Egypt? Would the child continue to be in danger despite their escape? Where would they live? How would they survive and have enough food to eat and clean water to drink? Even before arriving, the journey was marked with dangers, with robbers and heathens out to attack those who were courageous (or ignorant) enough to travel at night. There was nothing reasonably safe about the situation, and yet God prompted it, her husband listened with faith, and Our Lady did not question.

She prepared the little donkey, she thanked the women who had helped her with her newborn, gathered their few belongings, and covered her face and the baby with her mantel and cloak. Then she nursed and shushed him, "Please be quiet, my dear one, so that no one might hear you as we escape." And the baby Jesus was obedient to his mother, staying quiet and completely hushed in the dark night. Her heart ached within her: where was God during these dreadful moments? Right there in her motherly arms, and yet the consoling days of blooming with life had come to an end, and the reality of living with Jesus—the actual reality—called her to a more profound and immediate obedience and trust than ever before.

Nothing was prepared for them at the time of their arrival in Egypt, so they quickly and diligently put together a small home. They embraced poverty, and St. Joseph set out to work to provide what was needed. Our Lady shows numerous little acts of obedience in these moments: pressing out negativity, putting aside her questions about how they would make the income they need, or how they would even keep the child warm in the cold desert nights. Instead of burdening herself with questions and unknowns, she set herself to work to manage their home and pave the way for the income they needed to survive their new circumstances.

Her heart was well prepared for these moments, but it did not make any of these moments any easier. Her home in Egypt was temporary, she had no sense of timing in how long they would stay; no sense of if they would ever have the chance to return to their home in Nazareth to raise the child. So, she made a home with the little they had, she served St. Joseph, her son, and their neighbors as best as she could, and took care to make the newborn babe as comfortable as possible. In this, Our Lady sanctified the small moments of poverty we all experience at one point or another, by embracing the unknown with trust and obedience to what the Lord placed before her. "But I trust in you, O Lord, I say, 'You are my God.' My times are in your hand; deliver me from the hand of my enemies and persecutors!" (Psalm 31:14-15).

She kept her mind and heart on the wider picture of reality. She was the mother of God, and therefore she would create the best home possible for her little king in any and all circumstances. We might imagine her placing fresh flowers on a modest table and reaching out to the neighbors surrounding them who were also poor. She was residing in a community not her own, anticipating the future while staying present. We might hope that perhaps a neighbor baked bread for the new family and comforted the new mother with kindness and amazement that she had traveled so far despite just having given birth (for they did not know her secrets of just how the child was born). Our Lady would have demonstrated a humble confidence in relating their flight from home, and her trust in the new life to come. All who knew her were amazed at her wisdom and obedience under such circumstances.

How Might We Grow in Obedience and Discernment?

The beauty of obedience is that it is called for often in daily moments. How wisdom, intuition, and prudence grow from it is dependent upon the situation.

AUTHORITY AND DISCERNMENT

Whether someone is meant to be obeyed is the question first to consider. There are always those who have authority over others, over each man and each woman. It may be a husband to a wife, a mother superior to a sister or nun, or an employer to an employee. This authority acts as a map for good deeds and virtuous living, as a tent of protection over humanity leading to peace and all that is true. Recognizing authority and respecting virtuous authorities are necessary to grow in the spiritual life and a great part of the wisdom that women of virtue attain and live.

It can be noted here that there are some who are not meant to be obeyed. If, for instance, an authority is asking a man or woman to sin, to disobey Church teaching and Tradition, or to harm someone in any way (including him or herself), this authority figure is not meant to be obeyed. Of course, there is a certain level of knowledge and wisdom necessary to discern this.

Further, there are laws that those in authority guide others to obey and that they obey themselves. These rules, including faithfulness to natural law, are placed there for the protection of all and the dignity of life. It is precisely because God loves his people that natural law exists, and it is through charity that the Church relates to us these rules we must all obey, even if we do not fully understand.

Opening one's eyes to Church teaching on subjects like contraception, abortion, or the institution of marriage being between a man and a woman, are real-life tangible examples of the struggles faced in society today in light of obedience. Married couples in particular are on the front lines in the battle for virtue and must remain faithful to the authority of the Church in sexual morality. In the case of a man— and more particularly, a husband—he must look to the authority of the Church to be led along the path of sexual morality. He is called to protect the sacrament of marriage by staying faithful and leading his wife spiritually in this manner. Openness to life, for instance, is always necessary and the use of Natural Family Planning can be thoughtfully and prayerfully discerned between spouses with a nod to a husband's particular authority.

To practically grow in virtue, a woman might read through and pray with what is true, be it through the Tradition of the Church, official Church documents, the *Catechism of the Catholic Church*, or Catholic Scripture studies. A woman might consider taking up the Scriptures daily with a saint's commentary on a particular passage in order to grow and know the Word of God, as Our Lady knew the law. She might consider reading Church teachings on the difficult topics of our time in order to gain knowledge of the logic behind a particular teaching. She can take up the writings of the saints who have gone before us. With the foundation of reading and study, wisdom is attained as the mind and heart are more turned to truth and the ways of God. It is easier to practice obedience when we know why.

However, there are times the Lord does not reveal his reasons and simply asks for blind obedience, as he did with Our Lady in much of her life's circumstances. In these cases, and in situations where authority asks a woman to do something that is *not* notably wrong or against God's law, it is a significant act of humility and faithfulness to God to obey. The Lord has communicated numerous times to the saints and mystics the significance of obedience. Even in his appearances and various visions, saints would be instructed directly by Christ to do something, and their superiors would deny them. Christ always informed them that it was to their superior that they owed obedience. That is how powerful an act of obedience is, and how good for us it truly is.

The question now might be asked very personally: Who are my superiors? Who is it that the Lord has placed before me to whom I must be obedient? The next step would be to act in obedience to those people in those small moments.

Perhaps in the workplace, there is a project an employer would like finished by noon. One might do their very best to complete this task diligently. Perhaps a husband is asking his wife to purchase groceries that afternoon. She might create a list and buy those groceries as soon as time permits. Perhaps a mother superior is asking for a letter to be written and sent that day. The sister will use her time to complete it. These of course are specific examples for particular states of life, and yet within the day-to-day moments, each of us has opportunities to bring the spirit of obedience into our day. We can do this by being attentive to the duty of each moment and faithfully completing the tasks, chores, works, acts of service, and love we are called to.

THE GLORY OF OBEDIENCE

These seemingly small acts pave the way to great virtue, for Our Lady shows that it is her obedience in each moment—without question—that brought her to great moments and acts of blind obedience and trust before God, resulting in the glory of God and an everlasting crown as queen. The woman of wisdom knows this obedience to authority is not a threat to her dignity or independence of mind and heart. She knows that, in fact, it shows her preciousness—God has placed above her a superior to guide her, protect her, and lead her in the ways of truth just as St. Joseph was placed as an earthly authority over Our Lady.

The fruit of obedience and joyful submission is an interior God-given peace. Wisdom grows, the eyes of the heart see, ears hear and understand, as everything within is ordered sweetly. A humbling obedience naturally brings these fruits. It empties a woman of pride and fills her with the love and joy of God. It clarifies, bringing greater peace into daily moments. It acts as a safe road, leading along the narrow route to heaven. It draws us into the mystery of order that God created and deemed fitting for our well-being and good for the soul.

Our Lady's dignity, majesty, specific mission, and call were never harmed by her obedience but only enhanced and supported. A woman of virtue, by way of obedience, will grow in wisdom and discernment of what is good and evil. Through this process of listening to what is true, her heart and mind will become more acquainted with the ways of truth and her life will be lived in great wisdom. She will know what is right and what is wrong. Her conscience will clarify for her what should be done in each moment, and her maternal heart will radiate this wisdom and result in thoughtful advice for others, especially her physical or spiritual children who look to her for guidance and help.

Even more, when we walk the routes of spiritual darkness and lack a sense of the next step, the spirit of obedience leads us along God's path. Depending on her state in life, a woman might look to a wise parent, a spiritual director, a husband, or a superior to pray with her and to discuss what God is asking. She can be confident in the blessedness of those discerning prayers and conversations.

When we walk in moments of emptiness, spiritual poverty, or particular weaknesses, we might hold fast to the teachings of the Church, and in obedience, stay faithful to our daily prayers and works. This spirit of obedience, when well-ordered and joyfully practiced, brings an authentic freedom of spirit, a steady peace, a wisdom that is lasting and that can be passed down from generation to generation.

Our Lady, in humbling herself before the authority of God, the Old Law, and her spouse on earth, is a wise mother. Just as she passes on her wisdom to her sons and daughters, we too are called to be mothers filled with hope that we may pass on wisdom to our children, whether spiritual or physical.

CHAPTER 5

They Have No Wine

Imitating Mary's Unceasing Prayer
as a Persevering Woman

At the news of Herod's death, the Holy Family was able to return to Nazareth. Preparations to leave were made as fast as they came, and before they knew it, goodbyes were said to all those near whom they lived during that appointed time. They were able to return home under more peaceful circumstances. Returning home meant returning to relatives, dear friends, and neighbors, as well as a steady home in which to house the Holy Family; a place in which the child was meant to grow and flourish. They moved into their new house, which was rather dreary at first, but Our Lady would be quick to bring it to life in tending, tidying, and fostering beauty within her new modest walls.

In this return, she entered into the most hidden of days that she would experience in her motherhood to Christ. It was within those veiled days that she turned a simple house into a home with a faithful routine of work, prayer, and leisure, authentic peace, and a fullness of joy in the household. Though suffering had come to the Holy Family and would come again, all moments in time, all emotions, and all aspects of life would become a prayer because she would unite them to God's holy will. Following her example, we, too, learn the secret to serving, the secret to managing each day with strength.

Mary's Continual Prayer

It can often be tempting to think in this hidden and disciplined life with Our Lord, there was no laughter or moments of elevated happiness. To the contrary, perfection brought the ability to feel both deep sorrows and exuberant joys that were magnified and deepened. All of Our Lady's life, both active and contemplative, became a prayer, rising up as incense and bringing glory to God.

SEASONS

The hidden days in Nazareth were but a season in life. It was a time of joy and simplicity, a time of reprieve and rest for the hard work to come. Our Lady had, until that point, undergone the various trials caused by Herod's desire to destroy the Christ Child. She had left her home and been stripped of all that she knew, running hastily to a foreign land. She leaned heavily into her faith and trust in God's ways while not having any idea how long she would be away from Nazareth. Upon her return, the wine of joy filled her heart to the brim. After such perseverance through trials and worry, her heart was finally able to have a moment's rest. These initial beginnings were merely a foretaste of what was to come, and yet God does not ask beyond the limits of his grace. So there were a refreshing few years of reprieve and rest for this holy family, until the whispers of Christ's coming public ministry blossomed once again in the twelve-year-old Christ who remained behind in Jerusalem at the expense of his family's peace.

Every year they joined the caravan, the procession into and out of Jerusalem to celebrate the feast of the Passover. It is significant that the Holy Family lost the young Jesus in Jerusalem; a premonition of what was to come when Our Lady would lose his life until the glories of the resurrection. When Our Lady and St. Joseph lost the young Jesus, they were flooded with worry and searched anxiously for him, wondering how this could be and how they could lose him among family, acquaintances, and their kinsfolk. They returned all the way back to their initial starting point, walking back to the beginning. This diligent seeking went on for three days. Three dark days without him, three days signifying yet another dark night of Our Lady's soul and heart desperately wishing to be reunited with him. And yet her heart was completely tied to him in the perfect will of God.

When Our Lady was finally reunited with the young Jesus, she asked him why he had stayed behind and caused her such anxiety and worry. "Son, why have you treated us so? Behold, your father and I have been looking for you anxiously" (Luke 2:48). His response was simple, "How is it that you sought me? Did you not know that I must be in my Father's house?" (Luke 2:49). Upon hearing this reply, Our Lady did not understand him, but she held on to his words within her heart and wrapped her arms around her son once again. My son! she exclaimed with tears rolling down her cheek. And with this, it is revealed that in the moment where dawn breaks the darkness, in the moments we find Christ, we also are called to cling to our beloved and ask him with great love why he has hidden himself. That is the intimacy due to the love of bride and bridegroom; a clinging when found, a restoration of peace and joy expressed, and a wonder at why he had been away for a time.

He returned home with them and was obedient to Our Lady and St. Joseph, showing the circular relationship of love experienced by the New Adam and the New Eve. She was obedient to him, and he was obedient to her. Yes, losing the child Jesus in the Temple was an initial dark night of the soul in the pierced heart of Our Lady. Then, in that weight of her sorrow and searching sprung an exuberant joy upon finding her beloved son. In her heartache, her searching, her finding, her docility, her pondering, her actions became a consistent and persevering prayer; her life relaying a melody of highs and lows, and emotions of all ranges.

It would be a temptation to hold onto him, to protect him, to keep him hidden, but instead, the Blessed Mother supported his work and mission, even prompting him to begin it as her whole life and whole will were united to God's. In this union of wills, her words brought forth consistent prayer. Our Lady shows that all moments in time, all emotions, all aspects of life can become a prayer when united to God's holy will.

PERSEVERANCE IN PRAYER

The time came for Christ's public ministry. It was "not yet appointed" but was brought about hastily at his mother's request. They were attending a great feast of the wedding of a relative and the wine ran dry; a horror of embarrassment ran over the bridegroom as he realized. Our Blessed Mother, seeing him and his new bride in such distress, approached her son and said, "They have no wine." She knew what she was asking, and he knew as well. They exchanged glances. His response was for the whole world to hear she was the New Eve, the mother of the living whose request he could not help but to hear and act upon out of love for her. "O woman, what have you to do with me? My hour has not yet come" (John 2:4). Christ knew he would bring about this miracle before even attending the wedding, and it would be at the request of his mother.

She, being the mother of mercy herself, was prompted to request this miracle by the Holy Spirit, who placed this concern within her heart of sorrows, knowing her tenderness and care for what might at first seem to be a superficial concern. She cared deeply that the absence of wine would bring shame and embarrassment to the newly married couple, showing us that no issue is too small to bring to her and ask her intercession—her perfect prayer.

This initial request and prayer of Our Lady marked the beginning of Christ's public ministry. Christ took the water that had newly filled the purification jars and turned it into the sweetest and most fragrant of all wine. This mingling of water transformed into wine was the beginning of his ministry pointing to the end of his life; the crucifixion where his blood and water poured forth from his heart of compassion. Christ went from the work of carpentry to the heavenly father's work of redemption.

After the wedding at Cana, her role shifted to a quiet and hidden support. She was the mother of all mothers, the discalced Carmelite hidden away, the silent witness to all that was good, the weighty and hidden support of his redemptive plans. She stood behind him, as a creature, as his creature, with her heart and will tied to and united to his. She clung to the promise of the new kingdom to come; to the hope present in the Psalms, which she had memorized from a young age ... and she followed him. Her role was different from other followers, for she did not merely follow him but was the leader of the other followers in her own way through her prayer and perseverance at all moments. She was, of course, the most perfect of his followers. She served those around her, providing meals when she could, warmed cold hearts, and drew others to her son's teaching. All that she did, both active and contemplative, became a prayer because she united her heart and her life to her son's life perfectly.

Our Lady was a magnetic spirit that others wanted to be near, and her son knew this, for he had great and hidden plans of his own to give her as gift to all of his redeemed children. It was within this supportive role that we see the height of Our Lady's perseverance. She persevered through three years of ministry and of faithfulness to her role as woman and mother until the very end where she waited in hope during yet another three dark days.

How Might We Grow in Prayer and Perseverance?

Prayer is the fuel of daily life, the foundation of all. Like Our Lady, a woman must seek to unite her heart to Christ's heart in the stillness of meditative and contemplative prayer, in service to our family and loved ones, and in the joys of leisure and laughter.

SEASONS

All seasons of life require prayer. Unfortunately, at times, it can be a temptation to become impatient and expect unrealistic prayer disciplines in different seasons of life. For example: when I was single and newly married, I attended daily Mass, was faithful to my Holy Hours, and had an overall disciplined and blossoming prayer life. That is, until

I became a mother. In those early days of motherhood, I found myself holding a baby who fought sleep for hours upon hours, I was exhausted, and barely able to care for myself properly for a number of months. There came a point where I wondered if it was my fault that I was no longer able to attend daily Mass like I once did. I wondered if I simply was not pushing myself enough and was lacking in discipline, perhaps even offending the Lord.

Deep inside my heart was a tug-of-war between taking care of the baby and diligently fulfilling the prayer life I once had. It took some time and humility to begin to realize that the Lord was asking, during that time, for my submission to his will and to take on different forms of prayer more suitable to my season of motherhood.

Motherhood is mentioned here first because mothers have the most turbulent of prayer lives. A mother must stay vigilant to find times when frequent attendance of daily Holy Mass or Holy Hours is appropriate, and a mother must surrender those times she is found mostly in the home serving her family.

A single woman may have more time for prayer, or perhaps her working hours serve as an obstacle. Setting aside time for prayer becomes a bit easier when one has a consistent daily schedule than when one is in the changing seasons of motherhood. In the season of consistency, it becomes much easier to develop a prayer life that is extremely disciplined and in set hours of the day. The struggle will be to maintain discipline through times of consolation as well as times of desolation, or dryness in prayer. Nuns and sisters certainly have more time for this than any other woman, as it is time naturally carved out by the Rule. This is why it is easiest for a nun or sister to enter into the heights of contemplative union; there is simply more time to pursue it and more opportunities for the explicit pursuit of union with God! The widow also has a particular call to enter into greater depths, contemplating the end and uniting herself and her sorrows to Christ. A grandmother too has an ability to establish a routine that works within her own schedule. She might pray for the generations after her and for her beloved loved ones who have passed on. She might pass on traditional Catholic prayers to her grandchildren, teaching them, giving prayer cards, and acting as a spiritual support.

Each woman can safely understand that some prayers are more powerful than others (such as the Holy Mass) and recognize that in the ebbs and flow of life, she will be asked to say certain prayers more frequently than others. In light of this, there are two last parts that are worth noting: the first is that it does a woman no good to compare her prayer life with that of her friends and acquaintances. If she feels lacking and could do better, then she can examine this in her own heart (or perhaps with the help of a spiritual director) and commit to an increase in her prayer life in different areas. For example, if one is called to be a third order Benedictine, she will have certain prayers she must commit to with diligence to fulfill this call well. And another woman may be called to be a third order Dominican in which she would take a different approach and practices unique to their Rule. Each is unique and completely necessary as the members of the body which together make up the Body of Christ.

PERSEVERANCE

Since all women with the exception of Our Lady are imperfect, there will always at one point or another be difficult and trying times surrounding a disciplined prayer life. Change and transition can be a particularly difficult point in prayer, and this is where perseverance is necessary. We are called to practice a stubborn and consistent discipline. Often over the course of a vacation or time away from regular routine, prayer is dropped. If it is not due to the distraction and lack of routine, then it is through lack of time or relaxing of effort. It is in these moments that a woman is called to pray all the more. It might mean waking up a bit earlier or going to bed a bit later. It might mean pulling away from family for a quiet Rosary or morning prayer; no matter what it is, prayer must never be forgotten in the day.

In the midst of any distraction, life in any state is a call to patience and perseverance in prayer. The wife and the mother may find that household duties and children are a distraction, but there is a special note for these kinds of circumstances. Distraction and interruption are part of a mother's prayer. It is by and through these things, when born with love and patience, that a mother grows in patience and discipline in her prayer life by continuing to say her prayers despite the ongoing needs and noise. At the sight of a child begging for apple slices, a mother simply says, "I am praying now and will serve you later," or to a younger child, "Yes, I will cut this apple for you, and then I will be sitting here quietly to say my prayers." In her quick return to prayer, the action, distraction, and interruption become a part of the rhythm of her prayer, and the Lord sees it and delights in the details. Rather than being frustrated by these things, she might see them as opportunities to persevere in prayer and grow in the virtue of perseverance.

A woman is also called to turn to the Lord when suffering makes praying difficult. When I had my fourth baby, we were living in Austria. Despite the kindness of the doctors, there were a number of complications after the delivery, and in the middle of the night after a cesarean, we found there were serious issues that required another surgery. I was in so much pain, I could barely move or sit up, or even hold our new baby. My husband was in our flat twenty minutes away with our other three children because we had no family in town to help. I called him that night, telling him the complications were serious, and they needed to get me into surgery right away. He had to come quickly, and I needed him to pray and tell others to pray because I was completely frozen and flustered.

A pressure welled up in my chest as I thought about leaving him with four children and the weight of what we were facing. I couldn't pray. I was undone. It felt too hard. Over the course of those forty-five minutes, I cried and gave God my silence. I struggled to accept God's will and to say anything more than a desperate, "Jesus, help me."

As they were wheeling me into surgery just moments before I went under, my final prayer was, "St. Michael, be with me." And that was all I could say. Though it took quite some time to heal physically, all ended well, and one of the lessons I learned was that our desperate prayers in difficult times are notably powerful. Sometimes all we can give is a cry out and a desperate plea. That plea, the tears given to God, those moments we face within deep suffering, death, loss, or heartache are met by the Lord with tenderness and understanding. It is honest and good to admit to the hardship and let God into those little corners.

There are a number of difficult circumstances when prayer might be difficult. In this, we as women might unite our hearts to Our Lady of Sorrows and remember we are not alone. God in his tender love and mercy extends great compassion for these impoverished moments, and Our Lady brings light into what to do in each and all of these struggles. Suffering without Christ is just suffering, but united to him and given to him, it becomes a powerful form of prayer. It is by and through a continual—and sometimes daily—surrender that we receive the gift of joy in suffering made sweet, only possible through Jesus.

THE FOUNDATION OF SERVICE

Our Lady's heart was always united to her son's Sacred Heart, and she demonstrates that each part of life, in all moments, can become like incense and rise up as prayer. This frees the woman, in her humanity, to understand that no part of herself must be hidden from God, but on the contrary, when she brings all parts of her life to him, she is further purified in his love. It is in that daily communication with God that she sets a foundation for service and strength to manage the day ahead.

It is only by and through an interior prayer life that the work and mission of man and woman are ignited and fueled. A woman's prayer may begin with simple steps: a new commitment to a daily Rosary, dedication to morning and evening prayer, an examen of her actions at the end of a night, and a resolve to do or not do certain things the following day. Or perhaps they are more significant resolutions such as attendance of daily

Mass, a Holy Hour in the wee hours of the morning, or a commitment to silent prayer behind a closed door for a certain amount of time each day. Holy Mass is the greatest prayer we might participate in. In addition, the promises of a daily Rosary are powerful, and then, of course, spiritual reading is valuable: the Word of God, the lives of the saints, or devotionals to ignite a greater love and understanding in our hearts. All of these are good and beautiful, and all will bring grace upon grace into each day.

Prayer is the foundation of all service, and without it, nothing can be done well. The graces received in prayer cannot be achieved without prayer, and so to serve well a woman must always pray. No service, work, or mission can be perfected outside of God and seeking to do his will in all things. All service grows upon this prayer and perfects itself when prayer is the foundation.

Our Lady shows that in every state, in every moment, in all that a woman does, she is called to pray; that a whole life united to Christ becomes a continual prayer: in joys, in laughter, in celebration, in friendships, in relationships, and in sorrows, disappointments, suffering, illness, misfortune, and loss. There is no moment lost when a woman keeps Christ in the forefront of her mind and recognizes that he is a God of love who desires for her true freedom from sin and peace founded in a life of diligent and faithful, persevering prayer.

CHAPTER 6

Do Whatever He Tells You

Imitating Mary's Self-Denial as a Self-Sacrificial Woman

In her quiet life in Nazareth, homemaking matched with contemplation, Our Lady expressed the beauty of the wildflower: doing all small things with great love. During the Annunciation, she captured the receptivity of the lily: fragrant and receptive to God's holy plan. In the wake of the Passion of Christ, she captures the rose: strong, dedicated, with a disposition of restraint, denying even her natural instincts and uniting her suffering heart to Christ. Our Lady is the Mystical Rose, a woman willing to suffer, a woman who turns suffering into something fragrant and beautiful.

Being the mother of the Savior is the greatest honor a woman has ever been given and simultaneously the hardest life a woman has ever lived. Again and again, we see Mary denying herself what her maternal instinct wanted and receiving the will of God with joy and peace. It is in her example that we, in turn, find the key to freedom.

Choosing God's Will Above All

Her heart's rootedness gave Mary the ability to control her human nature and deny herself even the *very good* and *very natural* desires she had. This is notable through the Passion, but even in those early days of ministry she found she needed to restrain herself and let go of the one she loved, taking a role behind the scenes in order for him to fulfill his mission, and in order that she might fulfill her own. Her heart was sensitive and emotionally alive, but she never allowed her desires to rebel against God's will. In the years of her son's ministry and in the agonizing days of his Passion, she received God's will wholeheartedly.

As her son was obedient to the manual work he did in Nazareth, she too was also obedient to this quiet, unseen, and unheard-of work offering all of her actions to God diligently. She was disciplined, dedicating herself to the duty of each moment and staying present to each task she completed in the home and outside of it. She of course merited this focus, but that did not mean it was not challenged. In imitation of her son, she never found herself in a state of sin and always turned away from the enemy and his many temptations.

Once Christ entered into his ministry, Our Lady's role as a mother changed from being present constantly to being a bystander and supporter. There is always a transition in the relationship between mother and child when children grow and begin their adult lives. In obedience to this natural role of a mother, she also experienced this loss of intimate relationship in the quiet days of Nazareth.

"While he was still speaking to the people, behold, his mother and his brethren stood outside, asking to speak to him. But he replied to the man who told him, 'Who is my mother, and who are my brethren?' And stretching out his hand toward his disciples, he said, 'Here are my mother and my brethren! For whoever does the will of my Father in heaven is my brother, and sister, and mother'" (Matthew 12:46-50).

This moment is a pivotal example of Our Lady's surrendering spirit, her acceptance of God's will, and her choice to deny herself emotionally the natural tendency to cling to her son.

Her sensitive and feminine heart overcame the temptation to want what her son did not want even though her desire to see him was in itself good. It was not his will, and so his words brought yet another act of surrender on her part. When he refused to see her, she was not angry; her emotions remained subordinate to her reason, and she stayed at peace in obedience to what her son willed in that moment. She overcame bitterness, jealousy of the others around him, jealousy of his time, desire to be seen, and even being in a state of being rebuked she managed to receive this denial in complete and utter humility.

His ministry continued on in a separate but loving manner. She followed but not too close, so as not to smother him with her affections. She followed at the distance he asked that she follow and let her son fulfill the mission of God, uniting her whole heart with the Holy Spirit and loving selflessly; truly desiring what was best for him and the whole world.

THE PASSION

During the agony in the garden, as the disciples' eyes became drowsy, slowly drifting to sleep in the darkness of the night, Christ knelt in desperate prayer to his Father in heaven. He prayed, unifying his will to God's will. Even in the midst of this unitive prayer of the God-Man to his Father, his soul had a perfect disposition, yet his body reacted in complete and utter stress in exuding bloody sweat. His blood was already being shed at the beginning of his Passion, when he knelt alone, away from his friends, away from his mother, to simply reside with the Father and Holy Spirit. Nonetheless, his body longed for human consolation. Looking over to his sleeping brethren, he thought of his mother knowing that she stood by spiritually as a support but could not console him in this moment. Soon he was arrested, and "Simon Peter, having a sword, drew it and struck the high priest's slave and cut off his right ear" (John 18:10). Jesus, seeing Peter's good desire to save him, rebuked him, for it was not God's will, "Put your sword into its sheath; shall I not drink the chalice which the Father has given me?" (John 18:11).

Our Lady, at hearing of the events of the evening, longed once again to be with her son—this time in a more serious moment. She resisted. She chose to trust, surrender, and love the will of God above even her own. As Christ was thrown into the depths of anxiety to the extent that blood dripped down his precious and holy face, her heart sank into the depths at the news of the evening, her tears mingling spiritually with the drops of blood that had fallen from his face. This was only the beginning.

Our Lady in these moments shows the height of virtuous motherhood: she denied even her maternal desire, her *good* and *holy* and *feminine* desire to save her son, and instead continued to unite her heart to God's, experiencing fully the effects of the storm but denying herself the feeling of hopelessness or despair. She would stay in the peace of God; she would trust in his plan despite all of the unknown and fearful events to come.

Her heart spiraled interiorly, regulated by her prayer and heart's disposition. In her heart, she felt the dungeon where she united herself to her son now imprisoned. When Christ was arrested, how could she sleep? How could she rest knowing he was in danger and that these may mark the last hours of his time on earth in his human body? She knew in her depths what the arrest would lead to, it was the height of her son's mission, and she knew that she must deny herself her desire to throw herself in a fit of agony at his feet and scream for dear life for him to save himself for love of her.

As the night continued on, she resisted her desire to eradicate his suffering. Those hours though few felt exceptionally long, dreadful, and painful; her heart was filled with grief and longing to soothe him—to be with him as she had once been. Jesus lay within a jail cell awaiting his trial, in darkness, in the cold ... waiting. His mother, externally free to move as she pleased, knelt to the ground in her own agony, entering the interior dungeon of darkness within her heart, and she prayed. In this contemplative prayer, she met him, and she descended as he did into the depths of darkness—feeling in her bones all that was evil and prevailing that night. Physical distance of a jail cell did not prevent them from interior union. This was the first of many times where physical distance in the lives of the holy ones never stopped them from being where they were meant to be, allowing themselves to be moved in perfect timing, for instance, to meet the right person for conversion.

When the trial came, and the crowds pressed in to see what would happen, Our Lady restrained her external desires to save him, her body's desire to stand in front of each guard who would whip him, spit on him, mock him. She restrained herself from begging the soldiers to stop. She restrained her body from fainting in grief. She stood strong and sorrowful and was able to overcome all temptations to save him. She stood strong out of love, for love of God's will, for love of her children. She wants us to be happy with him in heaven as well, and the opened gates to heaven are through one road and one road only: the road of the cross.

A HEART UNITED TO GOD

Our Lady is the ultimate example of a pure creature whose body and desires were always obedient to her soul; the exterior being stabilized by the strength of the interior. This is the ultimate example of what happens when a heart is united to God. To understand this one must first look to her interior foundations and prayerful disposition both in times of contemplation and times of service. Her presence in each moment and clarity of mind steeped in reason led to the fulfillment of God's will always.

The word "pondering" itself reveals much about Our Lady's interior life. In all things, through all seasons, in her many works, in regular duties of a household, and the extraordinary responsibilities of suffering, "Mary kept all these things, pondering them in her heart" (Luke 2:19). Her hidden heart carried the treasures of the universe as she most perfectly united her heart to the heart of God. This quiet interior peace rose to the Lord as a fragrance rises to heaven, as a rose blossoms and reveals a sweet fragrance to those witnessing it.

Our Lady, who is essentially defined by her perpetual surrendering to the will of God, was the freest creature to have ever existed. It may be a temptation to think Our Lady was so strict and controlled that she must have been cross, serious, and rigid. On the contrary, she knew when it was a time to feast just as well as she knew when it was a time to fast. She knew intimately when it was time to weep and when it was time for laughter. She knew when it was time to mourn and when it was a time to rejoice. When it was time to meditate and when it was time to serve. She knew quite a bit about time and what she should be doing and when.

She reflected the very heart of his mercy by and through this perfect disposition and balance and she pleased the Lord in all that she did, thought, and pondered. Her pondering is none other than the heights of contemplation and unitive prayer. She meditated on the works of God, his ways above her own, and in her humility, she was taken up into the love of God most fully. This interior disposition resulted in her peaceful nature and exterior obedience to suffering and trials of life.

How Might We Practice Self-Denial and Self-Sacrificial Love?

In the eyes of the world, refusing to participate in sin looks to be the most constricted and miserable of lives. It seems so contrary to freedom to deny oneself what one wants, and yet the woman who is most free is the woman who is obedient to natural law, to reason, to goodness, and to virtue. There is a holy restraint and discipline that aids her ever-growing desire to know love.

IMITATING OUR LADY'S PRAYERFUL HEART

With her heart always united to God, Mary lived in freedom. She knew the right time for each motion of her heart. In imitation of this, the most practical manner in which a woman might attempt to use her time would be to take a retreat, seeking out the time to steep herself in silence and listen to what God is asking. With this being said, for most of us it is not often practical to take a retreat to find that silence. If this is the case, God will provide this path in the daily moments of any state in life, as long as one is attentive and actively seeks to know God's will.

A woman who seeks to imitate this sure foundation of prayer must seek to imitate Our Lady's pondering heart. The heart that ponders the words of the Lord, his way, his truths will be a heart steeped in the freedom of Christ. It is only by and through prayer and the sacraments that the mind is wiped clear of clutter, that the scales will fall off the eyes; the woman who seeks this virtue can see clearly what she is meant to do in each moment.

Getting back to first principles will be her surest foundation: God first, vocation second, works and hobbies third, etc. By sorting her priorities in line with God's plan, she begins to understand where her time should be placed and where it should not be placed. Both elements are important. In the rush of modernity, the ever-growing noise of the world, she will seek and pray to find interior silence to reside with her Lord and do what he tells her.

Prayer sheds light and paves the way to exterior action and enlightens a woman on what to do in her life and when to do it. The timing of everything must be continually discerned. Is it a moment of work? She will work diligently. Is it a moment of rest? She will rest well. Is it a moment of joy? She will laugh wholeheartedly. Is it a moment of sorrow? She will mourn and surrender. In addition to understanding the value of her time and where to place it, she will also gain self-knowledge in areas that need improvement.

With an interior disposition of pondering also comes an intimate self-knowledge, and insight into one's various weaknesses. Rather than being a discouragement, this knowledge is meant to bring light and healing to the soul. One's prayer must be strong and steady; it must be a daily discipline in order to become rooted. Silent prayer and pondering of God's Word, the examples of the saints, and the life of Christ, especially through the meditations of the holy Rosary, are direct ways to foster this steady rootedness in the Faith.

When a woman knows God's ways, when she understands that to reach the heights, she must first be silent, then she receives the treasure of contemplation. This is the highest form of prayer and a movement of the soul that is a pure gift from God. It is in this that desires are purified, and God's will is magnified in her heart; she begins to see more clearly, and her path is enlightened. This is significant as a single woman considers marriage or a religious vocation. It is significant in the vowed religious' ascent to unitive love with her spouse. It is significant in a bride's process of arranging life around the nourishment of her marriage, and a mother's discernment of how to guide, educate, and bring up her children.

GROWING IN SELF-DISCIPLINE

There are many on the ground, practical ways to overcome various weaknesses and sin in addition to praying for the graces. During prayer, a woman might consider where in her life she could be more disciplined. Is she overindulging in an area, is her prayer life suffering, or are her whims and desires causing a lack of contentment? All of these things can shed light on the coming steps to growth and change.

A woman who wishes to grow in self-discipline—a virtue that helps avoid so very many sins—might fast. The Church wisely gives certain seasons of fasting and certain rules for these seasons, for instance, abstinence from meat on Fridays. The first step in overcoming an over-indulgence is to fast in the opposite direction. If a woman tends to shop past her budget, she could fast from shopping for several days. If she is spending too much time on social media, she might fast for a set period of time. If she enjoys a little too much chocolate, she might take it out of her diet completely for a set time. During this set time—this season of fast—she grows new habits.

Fasting in each state of life is as unique as an individual person. A healthy single woman can individually decide which fasts are necessary, while a mother of a nursing child would be careful not to eliminate needed calories and food and so pick more creative fasts. In a healthy state a single woman who would like to fast from calories for a spiritual reason can more easily do so than a mother, or a woman who had difficulties with her relationship with food in the past. In these cases, a woman might consider different kinds of fasting rather than from calories. There are little disciplines and ways she might deny herself to grow in self-denial and discipline that do not involve skipping a meal. In the case of a sister or nun, it is not always possible to pick what food she will eat, and when she will eat it, so it is best to rest with the community's recommendations and follow her spiritual director's prompting for various fasts. In this case, fasts are more easily a part of the Rule and daily life, and in many cases, like the Carmelites, there are fasts that take place for their whole lives.

The key here is not to overreach. When forming a life of disciplined prayer and fasting, it is tempting to take on too much at once—a woman may look at the lives of the saints and see what she hopes to be but be careful not to overreach to the point of spiritual exhaustion or of simply not fulfilling the prayers and fasts she intended to do. Instead of shooting for the stars, a woman who wishes to grow in disciplined prayer and fasting might pick a few small prayers to add to her routine, or a fast that will be reasonable for her to complete, stretching her just a little bit at a time. As she grows in prayer and fasting, she might increase her spiritual exercises a little more and more.

This should be a lifelong journey of growth and may also be affected by setbacks from her state or vocation. An exhausted postpartum mother, a woman whose work grows heavy in different seasons, a sister who is sick and needs to rest her mind, or a grandmother feeling poorly—these are examples of when a woman may not be able to fast. In these cases, she is called to surrender to her state, seeing it as God's holy will and intentionally looking to pray and fast in the way God asks of her.

FREEDOM IN SELF-DENIAL

When a woman fasts from the things she likes, that are good in and of themselves, she is able to find balance. She will know when to shop, when to spend time on social media, when to enjoy a sweet treat. The self-discipline required for a fast frees the soul from being so moved by the passions and inordinate desires. Instead of indulging and letting the body demand what it wants, the soul regulates the body's desire and brings balance. This exterior action brings grace to the interior, and slowly but surely the exterior—the senses—learn to obey the desire of the soul and participate more fully in God's holy will.

While considering fasting, it is also important to consider feasting. A wedding, a gathering, and even the liturgical year provide the times of feasting to balance fasting. Our Lady at the wedding at Cana demonstrates quite simply the beauty of the feast and the significance of indulging in what is good in an ordered way. Fasting without feasting and vice-versa becomes rather lopsided and oppressive. This is where overindulging or excessive restraint leads to gluttony or scrupulosity— two extremes. Our Lady demonstrates this middle ground perfectly and encourages all to seek it.

This habit of self-denial, if cultivated, will pour out into a woman's actions, assisting her in the journey outside of herself, pouring herself into love of others.

We might note that the only place in Scripture that Our Lady tells her children what to do is at the wedding at Cana: "Do whatever he tells you" (John 2:5). She is always pointing to God's will and gently nudging her daughters. She is guiding, watching, and praying for all of her children. Her hiddenness and restraint demonstrate the modest woman that she is while setting the example for her daughters to stay humble in all things, all works, and all aspirations. It is God who raises up. It is God who magnifies. It is God who strips creatures of inordinate desires and purifies the heart to want what he wants. He helps us to find contentment in weakness while simultaneously seeking union with him and his will, which may at times be contrary to our own.

Self-denial does not come easily at first, but it grows by the grace of God and through the work of every woman who seeks to overcome herself. Once mastered, self-denial leads effectively to a great desire to serve others, to live outside of herself, and pour herself into those entrusted to her heart and home. She will become a humble safe haven, a little mother always pointing God's children to do what he asks of them. Each daughter of Mary will imitate her glorious mother by always pointing towards God's will in both times of joy and times of suffering.

CHAPTER 7

Mater Dolorosa

Imitating Mary's Purity as a Bridal Woman

In the darkness of Good Friday, Mary heard the call of him who loves her, "Behold, you are beautiful, my love; behold you are beautiful; your eyes are doves. Behold, you are beautiful, my beloved, truly lovely" (Song of Solomon 1:15-16). And her heart responded, "For your love is better than wine, your anointing oils are fragrant, your name is oil poured out; therefore, the maidens love you" (Song of Solomon 1:2-3). She was many things; a daughter ... sister ... bride; her purity of heart and bridal love were shown fully at the foot of the holy cross where she stood in complete and utter surrender. The mother of God remained faithful while receiving the fullness of a spiritual death within her heart. In the intensity of that pure love, every woman hears a call to follow the Mother of Sorrows, as a bride, into the arms of Christ, where she will find her true meaning.

Mary's Pure Love

Mary was the first to receive the blood and water which poured forth from Jesus' Sacred Heart and covered her whole being—clothing her in righteousness. Our Lady brought Christ into the world and watched him leave it; she witnessed the greatest beating heart, the Sacred Heart of Christ, stop beating for three days and three nights; she mourned fully the loss of her son and the life as she once knew it. She felt sorrow, suffered, and died internally while maintaining hope, joy, and peace through all of it. She is, in imitation of her son, a sign of contradiction.

There is no way this could be possible for a human being without receptivity of grace.

THE STRENGTH OF LOVE

She watched Christ scourged, and knowing the preciousness of his blood desired to wipe each drop from the cool marble ground as he was torn away from her, further and further away being beaten and bruised. In these moments she became more than his mother, she became the watchful servant, the faithful one, the woman whose *fiat* entered into the dark hour. They jeered at Jesus, they spit on him, they beat him, they mocked him. Every demon in the world took the opportunity to torture the king, and he had eyes for all of it. Christ was humiliated, and she was humiliated with him. He was misunderstood, and she was misunderstood with him. He was beaten, and her heart was beaten with him; bruised, bleeding, pouring.

The cross felt as heavy as the world, as it was the world placed upon Jesus' shoulder, and from afar she felt its weight. He walked and fell, she followed, and her heart sunk deep along with him into the ground ... lower and lower. How she wished to run and assist him, to carry it for him, to die for him, to take his place. He stopped a moment, and she stopped with him. He found her eyes in the crowd, and it was as if the whole world took a pause while mother and son stared deeply at one another, as he whispered silently to her heart: daughter, sister, bride.

The world shook at the sight of such love, for no one loves Mary more than Jesus. He experienced the deepest consolation during his Passion in the eyes of the woman and mother. She is, was, and always will be the only living creature that could never betray him. The mother—our mother—was his comfort, and one of the greatest gifts given to the human race. When their eyes locked, the purest of loves manifested in that stare. Their connection was as two hearts united; two hearts suffering all for the sake of love, for the sake of one another, for your sake, for the sake of the whole world. Her gaze was his chosen consolation, her gaze was his chosen protection, her gaze was his place of peace. It was a place of rest even in the midst of suffering.

There is no mother who would not die internally at the sight of seeing her son so tortured. If she were not full of grace, she may have died at the sight. Instead, she was strong with him, maintaining her disposition of surrender, like a jar fashioned in his hands letting herself be shattered across the marble floor as every drop of blood poured from her son's sacred body. She stayed by his side and never turned away.

The sight of her was his most perfect human consolation in his dark hour. Her fragrance penetrated the dry, dark air, but her soul radiated the light, and in his divine nature he saw this light and his human one received her consolation, as his mother. The sight of Mary's soul was as a magnificent garden of fragrance and beauty to be received. In the sight of one another, they continued forward to Calvary with a renewed strength that was only possible by and through true love.

As Christ was raised upon the hill, his hands and feet were pierced. These sacred wounds were still displayed on his resurrected body, showing that while the resurrection follows after the crucifixion, the wounds of love remain. His hands and feet, once little, fitting into her hands; the hands and feet she kissed as a baby, watched grow into those of a youthful young man, as he reached his age of prime; these precious hands and feet of her son were before her now, and pierced. She dropped to her knees and wept, yet her weeping was not for her, it was not in shame of her sins for she had no sin on her soul. It was in perfect compassion, perfect understanding of the depth of love that was brought forth out of the greatest darkness and the most evil act of mankind.

THE MOTHER OF THE LIVING

He took all shame upon himself, and her weeping took up the shame of her sons and daughters of the Church who wept for the sake of their sins in authentic repentance. The Church was in the act of being born through the hard labor of a mother whose tears and cries bore forth her many children, her sons and daughters. Jesus uttered few words in those final moments as his strength failed him, but he made sure to give the world a great gift, the gift of himself in the Holy Eucharist so as to show that he himself would remain with us. He also gave the world the most tender and perfect of mothers.

He stated it clearly, and his word is to be obeyed; to accept the great gifts he has given, to recognize them, and to cherish them is our duty. Our Lady "labored" during the Passion for the sake of her children's re-birth; she cried forth in pain for the sake of her children's new life. She was, is, and always will be the mother of the living. "When Jesus saw his mother, and the disciple whom he loved standing near, he said to his mother, 'Woman, behold, your son!' Then he said to the disciple, 'Behold, your mother!'" (John 19:26). She is mother, sister, and bride; Mother of God, Mother of the Church, and the Queen of Heaven and Earth.

Her disposition was courageous and sought no escape, but instead, she continued walking through the dark valley; she would labor and take on all sorrows for the sake of the birth of Holy Mother Church at Pentecost. For she was the mother, the woman who was first to be clothed in the Son, the New Eve brought forth from the rib of the New Adam, made alive by and through him. She is the firstfruits of Christ from the time of her conception in great anticipation for this moment in salvation history. This was her anguish; this was the delivery in which she suffered more than any woman on earth who has ever given birth.

Finally, at the three o'clock hour, he died, and the soldier pierced his Sacred Heart, and the blood and water gushed forth. When he was pierced, her heart fainted with love at the piercing she experienced in the depths of her soul at that very moment. It was a moment of desolate and desperate pain to match the ecstasy of union in their death, her heart united to his heart that stopped beating. Just as her son kept his sacred wounds in his glorified body, she in her assumed body kept the wounds on her heart, becoming for the world the *Mater Dolorosa*, the Mother of Sorrows.

On that ugly and marvelous day in which human eyes saw blood and water pour from his heart, her eyes saw more than just what the senses could detect. Christ's body seemed spiritually bright as light, blue and red light pouring forth over the whole world to bring a wealth of graces, a wealth of mercy, a wealth of love, and she felt that love pour from his whole self at the moment of his death. This ecstasy of flowing love and blood and water washed sinners clean, purifying the hearts of many so that they might be like the mother, sister, and bride who knelt below. She was a mere creature who remained faithful in all hours so that others might imitate her virtue, her purity, and the extent of her love for God.

How Might We Grow in Purity and Receive Christ as Bridegroom?

All women—all people—are all called to the banquet of heaven, the wedding feast of the Lamb, to union with Christ. These paths mark the beginning of a road ascending the high mountain of love; marked with self-sacrifice, suffering, joys, and responsibility. In these purifying paths that bring self-knowledge where weaknesses become known, there is a call for every woman to withdraw outside of the self and begin the purgative process to become Christ's little bride.

BRIDES OF CHRIST

A sister or nun is called to raise her heart and mind to the spiritual reality of her call as the bride of Christ. But it is not just a nun who is a bride of Christ. An unmarried woman or a woman who has consecrated her life to virginity is on a path that is meant to ignite the flame of service to those around her. A wife, given to her husband in marriage, has not met her end in that marriage but is meant to give of herself with the hope for the gift of new life. All of these states, these separate paths with unique individual missions given to each woman, are meant to lead to a single place: into the arms of Christ.

Our Lady as bride, most pure and perfect, fully knowing our sinfulness, hopes for each of her children to come to her son and be drawn into this purifying and unitive love. She desires all to seek him with their whole hearts. She desires to take each hand and place it into her son's hand; saying, "You are his, and he is yours." Her son whose hands remain wounded takes the hand of his little bride and works diligently to dress her in white; to wash the stains of sin and to encourage her by showering her with the graces that she prays for. The Mother beside him is the path to him and at the little bride's beckoning always answers in distributing the graces from her son.

The means and way to this union with Christ is by and through faithfulness to the primary vocation given to each woman, whether she is single, a bride, a mother, or in the religious life. She is called to protect her state in life with diligence from the outside world because there is nothing the devil wants more than for her to leave her post. Ensuring that her state in life is her primary vocation, she can then understand how the other parts of her life relate to it: her hobbies, dreams, relationships, and her work. All of these things should aid her primary vocation in one way or another and with grace proper balance comes (this balance will be unique to each woman and her particular call by God). She can be assured this balance is struck when she experiences a deep residing peace within her duties and work.

In no way does this mean it is easy, in fact, her primary vocation will bring a variety of challenges to strengthen her along the road. In the day-to-day moments, Our Lady takes her daughter's hand and guides her forward, as the surest and most certain path to her son. And yet how can this daughter, so sinful and frail, present herself to Christ in a bridal manner as Our Lady did so pure? She has no means to purify herself.

PURIFIED BY CHRIST

Christ is the one who will wash, clean, and clothe his servants in his majesty. The bridal woman, to receive such gifts, must be receptive and open to the gifts the Lord has in store for her. She must be wise. She must be prayerful, often pondering Christ's Passion and placing herself at the foot of the cross with Our Lady, filled with hope in times of suffering and darkness. The bridal woman must be surrendering; letting her worries wash away in the sigh of prayer and putting on the deepest trust in her savior.

But how might each woman, in any stage, grow in purity? When she first begins a more serious ascent to holiness, she might find her garments rather mucky, dirtied with the mud at the foot of the cross as she works diligently to climb the stairs of holiness by way of discipline and good works. The beginning stages of prayer are often difficult, but this should not discourage her; in fact, it should propel her forward to a place where good habits are formed, and meditative prayer comes out of discipline, a part of her routine. Soon the little woman of prayer, disciplined and not discouraged by her state, will till the soil at the cross. Her face will sweat, her body will be fatigued, and her garments will show the results of working in the mud. She who continues to work diligently and plant as many seeds within the tilled soil will keep hope, for when the rain falls little sprouts will appear in the ground and she will rejoice at the sight of such progress.

The rain brings on the flowers, and so in the day-to-day movements of life when suffering, trials, loss, and hardships overwhelm she must persevere in hope and pray diligently for it. The spring rain may bring dark clouds, heavy storms, and strong winds. These are the moments in life where she might be shaken, but holding fast and offering, surrendering, and uniting all difficulties to the cross turns all suffering into something rather beautiful. Never forget the beauty of the cross.

Before she knows it, before her eyes will appear the most elegant and lovely of flowers: roses and lilies alike, alongside small wildflowers representing her quiet daily sacrifices. These flowers will rise up as a fragrant garden around the holy cross, consoling the Sacred Heart of Jesus and Immaculate Heart of Mary beside her.

The good habits formed, the discipline in prayer, the daily meditations, the pondering of the cross, all these will move the Savior to wash the garments of this little woman, to make them white as snow and to say "they are finished" in the face of her repentance and tears. These tears will water the garden of her soul, and the Savior—the giver who will not be out-given—will continue to cleanse the garments of the little woman until she stands before him in dazzling white with eyes shining bright and a soul turned entirely towards her beloved.

The first step in this turning—this repentance—is to cleanse the bodily senses of all their various desires. The body so often wants what it wants and prompts the whole person to fall into sin. And yet the woman of valor is called to rise above her bodily desires and obtain the freedom that only manifests itself within the bonds of self-control. The beginning stages in turning from sins of impurity take a particular courage, as a woman must receive forgiveness in the sacrament of Reconciliation and like the lily's opening petals, be receptive to God's forgiveness.

When she leaves the sacrament of Reconciliation, she walks out as a saint, ready to begin anew and ready to avoid all stain as best she can. When the bad habits seek to manifest themselves once again, the courageous woman will run back to Jesus begging for his mercy, help, and grace. In meeting Christ in the confession, the humble woman begins anew, again, and again, and again. She ponders her life with some questions: Where are some areas I need to grow? What are my bad habits? How might I clear away these bad habits for good habits? What prayers might I say for this particular intention; to overcome these things that cause me to sin? And then once she ponders and prays for adequate self-knowledge, her own sinfulness, her own soiled dress that needs cleaning, her own sweat on her brow, her own attachments and sinfulness—then in that knowledge she is washed clean.

The woman depicted here, whose garments were torn and tattered, is washed in the blood of Christ, and by and through his mercy, she will be able to participate in this love by frequenting the sacrament of Reconciliation. She knows she can run to him over and over again and beg his forgiveness like Magdalene at his feet, wiping them with her hair and soothing them with fragrant oils.

TURNING TO THE MOTHER OF MERCY FOR PURITY

Like Magdalene, the courageous woman who seeks with all of her might to turn away from sins of impurity has a chance to stand, sit, kneel, and prostrate herself at the foot of the holy cross directly beside the Blessed Mother. Our Lady does not turn her away but instead embraces her in joy that she is there, and they can kneel in front of her son *together*; that they can mourn together, that the little woman can share in the sorrows of Woman.

Unlike the devils who condemn and arouse shame, Our Lady is the Mother of Mercy, and her gentle compassion is so easily moved when her little daughters ask for her help: "Mother, be my mother now." Our Lady, being the one without blemish, is eager to assist in overcoming all sin. She has a heart easily moved and no matter in what state she finds her daughters, she wishes to take their hand and help them onward in the pursuit of overcoming self.

She will help her children when called on to walk away from unhealthy friendships, leave relationships that lead to serious sin; to hate all impurity. She will help her daughter to expect in the men around her a respect of her womanhood, with fervent expectations for a man to protect her purity. And, with Our Lady's help, a woman will try to protect the purity of others through her demeanor, the way she talks, and the way she dresses and presents herself to the world. She will make sure to do her part and expect virtuous masculinity from her counterpart.

This purity will leave her eyes shining bright, capable of seeing herself, her sins—her frailties—and her many weaknesses, while simultaneously being courageous enough to accept mercy and to be receptive to God's love and to pursue him with all of her heart. The Lord will never overwhelm us in this process, but he instead works diligently like a loving father to encourage us to leave behind all that is ugly and take on all that is beautiful. Our Lady in this process is eager to distribute his graces and guide us along the right path; whenever she is called by her daughters, she answers diligently. In this process it is not we ourselves who can clean our garments, for it is he who meets his daughter as the beggar she is, sitting faithfully and stubbornly outside the castle gates. He is eager to wash her clean if she truly wants to be clean.

This cleaning will be necessary throughout her entire earthy pilgrimage until she runs and wins the race, having been inspired with complete and utter love. Then her heart will be fully united to Christ. In some instances, the souls of the great saints were wed to Christ on this earth. They lived lives of radiance reflecting Christ to the world, so evident in union with him as their bridegroom, stretching to reach the heights as the most perfect creature did, to be a bride like Mary. In other instances, the final purification must take place in the fires of purgatory, for a purification must take place before union with Christ can be achieved. As Our Lady was wed in loving union with God, her sons and daughters seek to make this ascent. In seeking to faithfully possess the heart of Christ the daughters of Mary might ponder the Song of Songs and hear the call of him who loves her, "Behold, you are beautiful, my love; behold you are beautiful; your eyes are doves. Behold, you are beautiful, my beloved, truly lovely" (Song of Solomon 1:15-16).

CHAPTER 8

Wounded by Love
Imitating Mary's Ardent Love as a Sensitive Woman

Our Lady fell down before the holy cross, head bowed low, knees to the ground, her whole body aching, shaking, sorrowful at the sight of her son whose breath struggled and then stopped. As she recognized before her the separation of soul and body, sorrow stabbed her heart. It was not the first time her heart was pierced by love and sorrow. All that took place prior flashed before her eyes and heart.

Mary's Sensitive Heart

She recalled his infancy, holding him in her arms, and the joyful days of delightful silence, contemplation, and service. She recalled love's first pang of sorrow, sharp as a sword in her heart when she presented Jesus to the Temple and St. Simeon predicted what was to come. His words lingered, and she again remembered them, "Behold, this child is set for the fall and rising of many in Israel, and for a sign that is spoken against (and a sword will pierce through your own soul also), that thoughts out of many hearts may be revealed" (Luke 2:34-35). She knew this moment, when St. Simeon prophesied what was to come and the magnitude of the mission of her newborn son. She also knew it would bring great suffering; nothing great is done without sacrifice and no love is met without responsibility.

Her thoughts streaked onward within her memory—the second arrow of love flying into her heart on her flight into Egypt. She recalled the unknown anxieties of a dangerous move in the night to a foreign land, leaving behind her kinsfolk and relatives, not knowing when she would return. She recalled Christ's childhood and the secrets of the days in Nazareth. She recalled the third arrow of love, and in this third arrow she lingered, and as she lingered on these memories bubbling up within her was a renewed and vibrant hope; for the story felt strangely similar. The third arrow of love brought the loss of her son whom she found in the end.

MARY'S HOLY CONCERN

He grew from an infant into a child, and child to a youth, and each year he celebrated the Jewish traditions and feasts until something strange happened when he was twelve years old. Our Lady and St. Joseph joined their kinsfolk in the caravan to journey back to Nazareth after the great pilgrimage and feast. Their travels would take a number of days, and it was typical to pass the time in conversation with relatives and friends, prayers, and chants. After a while, Our Lady noticed she had not seen her son in some time.

She walked through the crowds slowly at first, asking others if they had seen him. When it became evident he was nowhere to be found, anxiety beset the holy parents. Instead of proceeding forward as planned, they walked hastily backward through the crowds in search of him. They shouted his name, but he was nowhere in sight. They wandered their way through the crowds all through the day and all through the night. Our Lady's nights were sleepless, the boy was on her mind constantly. How could she sleep without knowing where he went? How could she have lost this precious child?

Finally, they arrived back in Jerusalem where he had remained while his parents journeyed home. Our Lady in this process experienced the desolation of the loss of the one whom she loved, of the one to whom she was so intimately and perfectly united, heart to heart—she sought him with everything in her being. One might say it would be most perfect if she had such extravagant trust to the point of being completely at peace in losing her son, but instead, God shows in this event that feeling care and holy concern over loved ones is proper, good, and beautiful. It is necessary to be disheartened and distressed at the loss of any soul, at the loss of any person, at the loss of what one loves; it would be inhuman not to be, even Christ grieved in the wake of Lazarus' death.

MARY'S TRUST

Our Lady shows her daughters the best way to worry. She never lost trust in God's plan but humbly received these three days of darkness even in her distress. Three whole days and three whole nights of toilsome darkness at the loss of her child. Where might he be? How could she have lost him? Was it her fault? Her prayers rose with a faith matched with concern, distress, and holy anxiety, all the while with trust in God's promises. She felt the emptiness once again that comes before the great gift of finding and receiving the Son of God.

She sought her son desperately: for three days and three nights, her lighted lamp guiding the way with her truest friend and beloved husband beside her, Joseph. When finally they found themselves back at the place they began their journey, they neared the Temple, entering and finding him among the scholars. He was there. The small boy suddenly seemed older, radiant in his youth.

Rather than finding him with other youth of his age playing in the walkways, or having stayed back without purpose, they found him in the Temple with the older wise ones, the scholars who knew the law by heart. He was not simply in the midst of the teachers, but he was engaged in discussion. Surely Our Lady and St. Joseph halted at the sight and before approaching him waited and watched. The scholars were in deep theological discussion and the youthful Christ in their midst was "listening to them and asking them questions" (Luke 2:46). His questions were not typical of a young boy his age. They were with purpose, quietly guiding them along the path of reason as their minds were illuminated and deep truths were revealed to them.

As the discussion came to a pause, Our Lady approached her son and said to him, "Son, why have you treated us so? Behold your father and I have been looking for you anxiously" (Luke 2:48). These are a treasure of words for all readers, as there are so very few words Our Lady says in Scripture. Make no mistake, Our Lady felt all of the human emotions, even to the extent of asking her son why. In his vibrant youthfulness he responded back to his mother, "How is it that you sought me? Did you not know that I must be in my Father's house?" (Luke 2:49). Though she did not understand why he had stayed behind, why he did not inform her as usual, she held these things deep within her heart.

This small manifestation of loss and gain proceeded what was to come at the holy cross. As she knelt before Christ crucified before her, this memory brought a bubbling of renewed hope. She would find him. She must find him. All was not lost, she persevered in trust and remained like the petals of a lily—entirely open to God's plan despite how painful it was in this moment.

MARY'S STRENGTH

It was the Passion that would bring the last four arrows, ultimately leading to the fulfillment of the prophesy of St. Simeon: the piercing she herself experienced in the moment of her son's death. She recalled earlier that dark day as she watched her son carry the cross on which he would be crucified. How she watched him fall to the ground three times, in complete and utter bodily weakness. Her heart was once again shot by an arrow at the sight—the fourth arrow to reach her heart. She watched the Roman soldiers nail his sacred hands and feet and lift high the cross. As they pierced him, yet another arrow, the fifth, flew into her own.

Could it be any darker than this? Why must he die such a horrific death? She thought and knew he was doing his work for his father's house. In all of this, her heart remained as a delicate flower. She maintained her sensitivity and emotion, kept her heart open and filled with love; she felt all of it in her depths most perfectly and reverently.

She resolved not to harden but to feel every pain, every ache, every hurt her son experienced and to feel it fully as his mother. Her tender heart was immensely strong. She received suffering upon herself like a wave breaking into the shore, bearing it with strength and maintaining her hope and receptivity to all of God's plan.

His precious blood dripped from his face as he was taken down from the wooden beams. She held the weight of his body in her arms, just as she had done when he was a newborn child. She recalled the early days of Bethlehem and his little newborn body pulsing with life. She recalled the hidden days in Nazareth filled with laughter, joy, sorrow, and work. She recalled how she had lost him as a young man and what wisdom he possessed. She recalled his public life of ministry, where the height of his work shown so brightly that the crowds had attempted to make him king. She recalled the dark moments of the past week as well: the betrayal of friends, the shouts of the crowds, the spit, the wounds, the weakness of his body before her.

What once radiated light and life had been emptied; his soul was absent, and with that he lay dead before her and darkness once again overtook the cloister of her heart in which the sixth arrow buried itself, this time piercing her so deeply she thought there could be no way to handle any more of this suffering. She gently wiped the hair from his face, her nurturing, maternal spirit unable to resist. And she wept.

Her love and faithfulness to her beloved led her to the cross where she was martyred on the inside. The hiddenness of her own spiritual martyrdom reflected the weight of her womanhood, her heart-suffering remained completely hidden, unadulterated, unseen, a mystery veiled until the appointed time. The tears she shed were obvious to all, but the figurative blood of her interior death was never seen by man. She was too precious to be seen in full, it was all too sacred that even her spiritual martyrdom remains veiled to the world, misunderstood by so many. Her tears fell onto his precious face, one after the other, cleansing it of blood.

Her cries at the cross flowed from her perfect compassion as she suffered with her beloved, delicate as a rose, terrible as an army. She would not move; she would not cease to love. She was wounded. She was wounded by love.

How Might We Grow in Ardent Love and Keep a Sensitive Heart?

There must always be a proper balance of maintaining the boundaries of one's heart, of keeping watch over emotions and desires and allowing the Lord to penetrate each one. There are things a woman may want that God does not want for her. The process of discernment, keeping vigilant about where she is meant to serve and whom she is meant to serve first—God—will be her guiding path and a helpful light to lead her to greatness of virtue, setting her heart aflame with an ardent love for both God and neighbor.

DISCERNING HOW TO LOVE WELL

The single woman, rather than looking towards the future in a state of anxiety, can rest in her state by seeing the time she has as gift. She might certainly be busy with studies or work, she might have several friends with whom she is able to spend quality time, and she may even feel strained for time. Nevertheless, she does have a particular time that other states no longer have. This is the gift of being unattached, in which the single woman might find rest. To increase in love and move outside of herself the single woman might use her talents to give back to the community. This might look like service work and volunteering, or it might be achieved through her studies, work, or career. In any case, the gift of her service is especially precious and benefits her greatly by engaging her maternal nature and living it out most fully within her state. The foundations of service lie in the sensitive heart of woman. In looking towards others, seeing a need and practically caring for this need, she gives a gift of self. This offering of service is a gift to her family, her friends, her community, and the world. It is in her gift of service where she offsets self-love with selflessness and therefore imitates Our Lady in her daily service in Nazareth.

The wife and mother are called to a different kind of service. Her primary work is to serve her family, and in that, she will grow in ardent love. The people entrusted to her act as Christ before her. When she serves her husband, she serves Christ in him. When she serves her children, she serves the Christ child in them. There is a natural movement of the heart in a desire to serve by love. She is sensitive to the needs of her husband and children, and her service to her family continually purifies and uplifts her own soul.

There is a gift of clarity in family life regarding what she is meant to focus on and where the virtue of love may grow. She knows who matters the most, whom she should be serving first, and her life becomes increasingly harmonious and peaceful the more she keeps this perspective. This in no way indicates that she might not serve outside of the family. There are many particular circumstances that lead to other works, hobbies, volunteering, or paths that she might take according to God's mission and will in her life, but as she sets her eyes on her primary vocation, all will take shape beautifully and peacefully and her work outside of it will be fueled with grace. A wife and a mother, when prompted to work outside the confines of her family, must be careful and discerning of whether it is her will or God's will; the desires of the heart must continually be purified.

A sister or nun is in the most restful of these situations. It is within her Rule, her chastity, obedience, and poverty that she grows in ardent love. This love is directed towards her divine spouse where she rests in the heart of the Lord. Leaning into obedience, she knows what she certainly needs to be doing in each given moment. Her duty of the moment and the tasks in front of her are purified when she seeks to do all with excellence fueled by love. Her perseverance in the Rule and obedience to her superior will bring great opportunities for her love for the Lord Jesus and the love for her sisters walking the journey of holiness beside her to increase. In her particular faithfulness to the life of prayer, she will be drawn higher on the mount of holiness, her love will continue to be purified so that her self-love is eradicated to make way for ardent, true, and selfless love to capture the whole of her heart.

Every woman might take note of the lives of the saints and be on guard to protect her state from distraction and be discerning in all that she does. St. Thérèse of the Child Jesus had a primary vocation as a Discalced Carmelite nun but also was a writer. St. Teresa of Avila, rather than staying in her main house and fulfilling regular duties united to the Rule of Carmel, left her monastery to reform the Carmelites. It must have been quite a rebellious action initially, and if it was not in keeping with God's will, she certainly would have lacked the graces necessary to achieve all that she did. She kept her Rule as a Carmelite and also reformed the order, wrote books for her sisters, traveled, and did all sorts of things Discalced Carmelites are not usually called to do. With her heart open to the promptings of God, each woman must discern whether her desires are according to God's will; her sensitive heart must beat in time with God's call.

LOOKING TO MARY FOR THE STRENGTH TO LOVE WELL

In every state of life, a woman can live for herself or give over her life for those she loves. Her sensitive heart is a heart of flesh, pulsing, living, and ready to receive and nourish the souls entrusted to her (whether those souls be acquaintances or strangers met on the street, or the children, relatives, and friends closest to her). She is called to give—to give of herself and live outside of herself in a state of flourishing love.

This sensitivity towards others is a way in which a woman can gauge emotions, and it is a great power, for she can use this power to hurt others as well as to receive and welcome them. She can lean into compassion or fall prey to the exercise of rash judgment. She can be moved by love or allow her heart to calcify. She can forgive or hold a grudge.

There is a superficial kind of sensitivity that gives rise to self-love. This kind of sensitivity, rather than bringing a woman outside of herself and drawing people together, is divisive and pushes her back inside of herself. It is a temptation all of us face at one time or another. To overcome this particular defect, one must dig down to the roots of the issue. This kind of passion is self-serving, is easily wounded by the words or actions of others and is rooted in fear—fear of wounded pride, fear of not being loved, fear of rejection.

Life will often bring sudden twists and turns at times, and all people need healing in Christ. In the wake of suffering and deep wounds, it becomes easier to harden ourselves rather than to feel, it is easier to shut others out rather than to receive love from those close to us. In the face of suffering, Mary shows her daughters the way of maintaining a heart of selfless love. When she lost the youthful Christ in Jerusalem for three days, she did not feel slighted, forgotten, or poorly loved. Our Lady surrendered, allowing her pain to penetrate her heart and pour forth in trust, understanding that God's plan and paths will not always be fully understood on this earth. At times, they hurt.

LOVING IN THE MIDST OF SUFFERING

When a mother loses her child, it cuts something so deep within her very core. A mother cannot help but feel, even if she lacks the understanding of why a hurt exists so deeply within her. This is the sensitivity that a woman who loves her child will feel; she will feel this love and longing, and she will ache at any loss, no matter how small the child. At times these wounds of love feel overwhelming and all too much. She may feel desolate, dark, like God has left her to suffer and there is nowhere to turn but inward. It is within this state that the Lord wishes to shock her with love. He wishes to draw her into the deep mystery of purgative and purifying suffering that not only cleanses her soul but can save the souls of others when united to the holy cross. In the case of a mother who has lost her child, that child becomes a little lighthouse leading her home, pointing to eternity, and reminding her this is not the end.

Many times, healing takes place through a kind of spiritual surgery. Take, for instance, a single woman who must walk away from a disordered relationship. She knows inside the man she is leaving is not the one to marry and yet it hurts deeply initially because of her love for him, the time they spent together, and the memories they shared. He may repeatedly flash before her mind's eye, and she may find herself hurting and sulking in this malaise. If she meets someone else later on, she will be able to see then that this loss was precisely to make a moment like this possible, this new moment that God had chosen for her. She will have found her vocation. This initial loss is a kind of spiritual surgery, a cutting away of what is harmful so that now her heart can pulse with life. Instead of experiencing a hardening of heart, she will be able to say yes to the next opportunity; she will be able (in time) to let herself love again.

In the wake of the Passion, Mary watched and hurt, and stayed and hurt more, and knelt to the ground and hurt even more. It was another round of emptying in her life, another round of surrender at its greatest capacity. Rather than *not* feeling the pain of her son and instead hardening herself to what was happening before her, she let herself feel all of the maternal love a mother could ever feel and be wounded by this love in the depths of her being. Her act of hope would be impossible naturally, but due to the extent of her love and her role as mother of Christ—mother of the Church, mother to her many sons and daughters—she was able to accept the piercing arrows of suffering while keeping a heart of flesh, a heart that *feels*.

A woman's heart in its pure state is a sensitive, tender nurturing place for her children to rest and grow, both physical and spiritual children. There is a certain delicacy that comes with this tenderness and gentleness, this openness and receptivity to others. All these traits are intrinsically linked to the qualities of femininity that make a woman fit to be a mother. It is in the gift of self, of joyful service, of pouring into those she loves that a woman's heart softens and expands in love.

All of this—the receptivity, kindness, gentle nature, and sensitivity—are meant to harmonize with a woman's natural strength, rootedness, and courage. It is because of this that Our Lady's heart reflects both the delicacy of the rose petal and the strength of the thorny stem rooted deep within the earth. She was sensitive yet strong, as we—her daughters— might pray to be as we seek to imitate her. When suffering and trials came, she was able to hold fast to hope in even the most hopeless moments thanks to this graced balance of attributes.

CHAPTER 9

My Daughter, I Love You
Imitating Mary's Patience as a Nurturing Woman

The worst was over, and the Sabbath day brought a deafening silence to the mother of God. Her heart had died, and her arms were now empty. She remembered the promises of her forefathers and the kingdom of heaven her son had promised, and with unwavering hope, she waited. Kneeling beside the most Blessed Mother, who had just been given to the whole of the Church as both mother of God and mother of the Church, knelt the very little daughter Mary Magdalene. Mary tenderly encouraged her daughter Magdalene, and in the patience of Mother and daughter, we find what our maternal spirit is made to do.

A Nurturing Mother

Magdalene had been a sinful woman, infamous in her own right. She had, as a sinner, come courageously to meet Christ, unknowingly and mystically preparing him for this moment of his death. She brought a jar into the home where Christ was dining, the home of a Pharisee. She stood behind the Lord and placed herself at his feet weeping as "she began to wet his feet with her tears, and she wiped them with the hair of her head, and kissed his feet, and anointed them with the ointment" (Luke 7:38-39). This perfume acted as balm, as ointment foreshadowing the ointments and fragrance that were to be used at his burial. She approached Jesus in gentle confidence, a sinner and a stranger to all that was good, only to find her whole life turned around.

THE COURAGE OF A DAUGHTER, THE TENDERNESS OF A MOTHER

Her past would no longer haunt her as she did something quite courageous, a thing only the brave can truly do. It is brave to receive God's mercy—something that seems so easy but is lost in the temptation of scruples, the impatience in the journey of perfection, and the difficult pursuit of self-knowledge. All of these are washed away in the mercy of Christ, in the authentic tears of repentance, and a holy confidence and hope.

After this great event in Mary Magdalene's life, she laid down her life for her Lord. Clinging to Our Lady in her darkest hour with her son, watching the mother of God cry out as she felt her heart pierced in martyrdom, she knelt by her side and would not let go. At the sight of the injuries of Christ, she never turned her eyes. She sighed and dropped into Our Lady's arms, giving herself mystically to the Blessed Virgin as her new mother.

Throughout the whole of the Passion, Mary Magdalene followed Our Lady, wept with her, knelt with her, prayed with her, and in the midst of such desolation as she watched her beloved Savior die, she did her very best to maintain a disposition of hope and trust like Our Lady. Remembering her repentance, she embraced the mother of God as her own. Her sinful past had been wiped away, and Magdalene's holy confidence was palpable as she approached Christ and stood with Mary at his feet, setting an example that all men and women must follow.

Our Lady turned to the girl tenderly. When Christ handed over Our Lady to St. John, her hidden mission was brought to its earthly pinnacle. She was the mother of the Church, she was the New Mother of the living, the New Eve who turned back the primeval disobedience to obedience, offsetting Eve's no with her yes. Following this example, Magdalene, as a woman newly dedicated to God, knew she wanted to be like Our Lady. She clung to her as Ruth had clung to Naomi, "Entreat me not to leave you or to return from following you; for where you go, I will go, and where you lodge I will lodge; your people shall be my people and your

God my God" (Ruth 1:16). Our Lady took Magdalene as her daughter as Naomi received Ruth. Mary was Magdalene's new mother from this point forward, and she would teach Magdalene her ways, teach her of God, and teach her holy womanhood.

Even in the midst of her own suffering, Our Lady looked outward to others and took Mary Magdalene in. She wrapped her arms around her at the foot of the holy cross just as Christ received this young woman. These moments changed her life forever, as tradition holds that after Christ's death, Magdalene ran deep into the desert to live the rest of her days as a hermit. Our Lady looked deep into Magdalene's eyes now radiating with grace that only comes by true repentance; she knew this was the daughter who stood for every woman who would run to her. She thought simply, she said simply: my daughter, I love you. These are words that echo to you and echo to me, as children under the care of a tender and selfless mother.

THE PATIENCE OF MARY

Seeing these women mourning, Joseph of Arimathea came to assist and offer his strength. He asked permission and was able to take Christ's body from the holy cross so that his loved ones might prepare his body for burial. When Jesus was taken down from the cross, his body fell into the arms of his mother. She held him, heavy with death, and recalled him as a newborn child. In this moment time seemed to stop as those around watched this encounter between mother and child with reverence and modest reserve. When the time came Joseph of Arimathea, moved by all that took place, wrapped Christ's body in a linen shroud and held him in his own hands to bring him and lay him in the tomb.

The women followed mourning and weeping. Our Lady watched her son laid to rest in the tomb, and her heart felt the sliver of the final arrow bringing the totality of her sorrows to an apex. Her son was dead. Instead of turning inward, she thought of Magdalene beside her, who had followed alongside her. She comforted her with her eyes of tender love and nurturing maternal spirit, and Magdalene also comforted this mother with her presence, persistence, and sharing in her sorrows.

In an effort to lay him with the deepest reverence and tender care, the women went quickly to prepare spices and ointments to give him a proper burial. According to the law, they rested on the Sabbath before returning to anoint the body of Jesus.

This Sabbath was a day of heavy silence for the mourning mother. She waited longing for what was to come, though she did not know what exactly would come. She felt every maternal cry for the life of a child in every ounce of her being. She waited. She prepared for the Sabbath to end, and then waited obediently according to the law. She clothed herself with patience through the trial of deep and relentless suffering.

Her holiness, her fragrance, her spirit poured forth as a sweet ointment rising to the heavens. In those moments of patience waiting for what was to come she wept bitterly in the darkness. Her heart, so united to the son, dwelt in the darkness of death, awaiting the return of the light, as the moon awaits the return of the sun during the darkness of an eclipse.

The consequences of her *fiat* resounded through the world like drums making soldiers ready for battle. Finally, the Sabbath that nearly suffocated her Immaculate Heart had passed, and the day of light took place, where her little daughter Mary Magdalene saw her way to the tomb to anoint his precious body, only to find it was emptied. Our Lady was not there in this moment. St. John Paul II suggests that this is because she had already seen him, as she had been there through all of the events of his Passion, and if she had thought him still dead would have gone with the other women. In his own words, "Indeed, it is legitimate to think that the Mother was probably the first person to whom the risen Jesus appeared. Could not Mary's absence from the group of women who went to the tomb at dawn (cf. Mk 16:1; Mt 28:1) indicate that she had already met Jesus? This inference would also be confirmed by the fact that the first witnesses of the Resurrection, by Jesus' will, were the women who had remained faithful at the foot of the Cross and therefore were more steadfast in faith."[3]

Tradition holds that she saw him in his risen state and bowed low with fear of the Lord as she trembled in astonishment, her whole body filled with hope that manifests into reality. Our Lady's receptivity and surrendering spirit received life once again, and the reward of faithfulness, patience, and obedience brought her into this moment of joy and utter amazement.

The trials and suffering brought her to the fulfillment of his promise to rise on the third day. Obediently she continued in her quiet, receptive, and contemplative nature. Her mission before her was not fully accomplished and had truly only just begun.

THE CALL OF MAGDALENE

Very early on the first day of the week, in the quiet of the morning hours, the birds chirped, and darkness swept the earth for only moments longer, as sunrise quickly approached. The women had gathered and brought with them all of what they would need to return to the tomb of Christ. As they walked along in the dark, they wondered how they would roll away the stone, as they were women and bore not the physical strength of man. When they drew near, they saw the stone had already been rolled away and they looked on wondering what had taken place. When they entered the tomb, they saw in the darkness a dazzling light and from the beings before them came the words, "Why do you seek the living among the dead?" (Luke 24:5).

Magdalene knelt down weeping when she saw the empty tomb. She did not yet understand and thought the Lord's body had been taken. The woman out of whom seven demons were cast again gave Christ her tears, and in response, Jesus appeared to her and called her *woman*, asking whom she was seeking. He indicated the deep mystery of her coming to be fully who she was meant to be: casting off sin and putting on the virtuous woman. She thought he was the gardener. Then he gave her the title of all titles calling her, "Mary," calling her by name since she had turned from her ways and become like his mother. This name represented the truth that all creatures are called to holiness, to become *like* the most perfect created being. The call to all women is to bear fruit and become like *Mary*.

How Might We Grow in Patience and Embrace a Nurturing Spirit?

Now more than ever modern souls need the example of Mary Magdalene. No matter the state or extent of sin, no matter how far or near, she sets the example of honest repentance and imitation of Our Lady. No sin is too far from the chance to return, to change, to repent, and no woman is so close as to reach the height and depth of God's love for Our Lady. Each cup will be filled, but not all cups have the same depth. God loves Our Lady more than any creature on this earth—for none have been given gifts as great as hers. Her cup is the greatest that will ever exist, yet even so, every cup (every soul) is meant to be filled and overflowing. Mary Magdalene was inspired rather than discouraged by the sight of Our Lady's perfections.

BECOMING A WOMAN ALIVE IN CHRIST

In the ugliness of her sin, she knew she wanted to be what was beautiful. She did not care what others thought. She did not mind the Pharisees who condemned her presence. She allowed herself to be humbled and approached—no—hastened to Christ with a holy confidence wiping his feet and seeking to know him intimately and vulnerably.

This holy friendship is the type of friendship in which Christ calls all to himself. He desires to stir in his daughters a love that seeks his mercy in all things. He desires that in meeting mercy a change of heart takes place, and he desires his daughters, like Magdalene, to follow the path to holiness, leading to the holy cross and beyond.

It was in the sight of Our Lady that Mary Magdalene knew what she wanted to be. It was in the sight of all that is true, good, and beautiful that Mary Magdalene repented of her sins. All women, like Mary Magdalene, are called to a holy and humble repentance, a turning away from sin over and over and over again. All women are called to imitate the Mother of the Living by becoming a mother made alive again in Christ, turning from evil and putting on the virtues of all that is good.

Mary Magdalene casts away evil for virtue and turns from sin, offering her whole life to God. In this process of purgation, she puts on her deepest form of humanity, becoming woman and in that embracing the natural qualities of women, one of which being a nurturing and maternal spirit. In meeting Our Lady, she met her mother and followed her along Our Lady's darkest road to Calvary where her heart mourned alongside the Mother of God.

There is no woman other than Our Lady that is unwounded, untouched by sin, who is not in need of some healing. The sin in a woman's life brings with it a darkness permitted by her actions, a door opened to evil that must be cast out. Once cast out, there is a continued process of purgative love and a call to a deeper union, a longing for Christ above all, and patience in all trials. Each woman is like Mary Magdalene and each woman has a choice to be like Eve or become like Mary.

BECOMING A NURTURING MOTHER THROUGH PATIENCE

To grow in patience, a woman must go through some trials or suffering in life where she might practice that patience. If a woman loses her work and desperately needs the income, she might practice patience by surrendering each new day in the sight of her anxieties. If a woman is experiencing an onset of difficult health problems, she might put on patience by doing her very best to care for herself while accepting the circumstances into which she has been thrust. She will do this for the sake of glorifying God and will unite her sufferings to the holy cross. To grow in patience a woman who is eager to marry and has not met her spouse must hand over this desire to Christ that he might lead her along her path peacefully, putting off all anxiety for the future. Patience is a constant and consistent act of surrender, and in most circumstances, this surrender needs to happen over and over again in various trying circumstances.

But as in all of this, in all suffering and life's various trials, a woman can receive the comfort of a mother in the heart of Our Lady. She is the mother ready to nurture her in all circumstances. When a woman lies awake at night pondering her current sorrows, childhood trauma, the hardships of the day-to-day, the loss of a loved one, or her failing health, she might pray and picture the Mother of God sitting beside her bed. She might lay her head down on her lap and receive the nurturing mother's tender care. Just as Our Lady encouraged Mary Magdalene, Our Lady is eager to encourage all women.

If a woman chooses to receive this love and this mercy and tenderness from the Mother of God, she will surely be more able to extend it fully to others. A nurturing and maternal spirit is woven into the fabric of the feminine soul for the sake of gently lifting up others.

In each woman's life, there will be those entrusted to her care. The maternal woman will exude a nurturing spirit, ready to encourage and uplift. Part of being a nurturing spirit is to avoid gossip and the detraction of others. It is to breathe life into conversation and be filled with kindness. This is not to say a woman might not discuss something bothering her at length with a spouse, trusted friend, or spiritual director. But if she finds herself in the midst of a conversation that centers on the detraction of a soul not present, she might exclude herself from the conversation, try to change the topic, or say something kind about the person being discussed. In the same way, a wife might be careful to speak well of her husband. If she is going through various trials within her marriage, she might discern whom to speak with more openly, for even though she is never meant to bear all things alone, she will also want to avoid various groups where "husband bashing" takes place. The nurturing woman hopes to protect the reputations of others, gives others the benefit of the doubt, and is encouraging in all things good, true, and beautiful.

There is no life lived that will not need to bear the faults of others patiently. No woman apart from Our Lady is perfect, and one simply cannot expect perfection in others. Therefore, it is most powerful to forgive quickly those whom the Lord is calling us to forgive. At the same time, we must peacefully put into place appropriate boundaries in relationships that might cause too much pain due to the evils of sin and fallen nature. Every woman must bear with others patiently.

First of all, however, she must be most patient with herself. Sometimes a woman might find herself so eager to run to Christ, as did Magdalene, and so eager to be his perfect daughter that she finds herself growing scrupulous and impatient with her journey in holiness. To be patient in the spiritual life is to accept her weaknesses, sinfulness, and frailty as the exact weaknesses from which she will turn away and grow holy.

It gives Christ great joy to see the sinner turned saint, to see a woman who struggles with losing her temper instead temper her emotions over time and be vigilant over her passions. This overcoming is a powerful process that brings God glory. In much of the case, it takes time and extensive efforts, it takes pain, purgation, suffering, and most of all it takes patience.

Like Our Lady on Holy Saturday, a woman is called to a spiritual patience in this purgative darkness. If a woman is patient with herself while still maintaining a holy zeal and longing for holiness, seeking God with all of her heart, she will more fully practice patience towards others, who are also sinful and fallen. The fruit of hatred of sin is a zeal for perfection. The fruit of patience towards oneself on the road to perfection is being patient towards others on their own journeys, and the fruit of this patience as a whole is the maternal nurturing spirit. It seems so simple, and yet we need our tender Mother's patient care to help us to accept God's undying love and mercy.

CHAPTER 10

The Valiant Woman

Imitating Mary's Angelic Kindness as a Strong Woman

The days after the resurrection are wrapped in joy, glory, rejoicing, and mystery. There are many stories, miracles, and moments related in the Gospel, yet the writers acknowledge that there was so much more that they were not able to record, and these things are kept as a precious mystery, only to be revealed in heaven, and at the end of time. It was during this time, before Jesus left and sent the Spirit, that Our Lady's own heart expanded further in love for his beloved disciples.

She looked into each of their eyes as she looked into her son's, embracing each of them as her own. Love expanded in her heart as she awaited the bearing of new life in the form of the Church. She is the Mother of the Church, and in her heart, flaming with a love that is strong and fiery, we find our mission as her children in the Church.

Mary, Mother of the Church

Christ ascended into the heavens, and Our Lady watched as she called to mind the many times he had left her previously, but this time the pain was bittersweet. She pondered what was to come and the work she would continue to do in order to build up the Church in her womanly way: to be there for her children, to tell the stories of his childhood to his disciples, to share the secrets of her heart to the hearts of saints, to be a source of wisdom, kindness, and generosity to all of those who approach God in true humility, fear of the Lord, and poverty of spirit.

PENTECOST

Her work continued, and when the day for the birth of holy mother Church came, she was renewed as the Spirit once again overshadowed her, this time with even greater fullness. He came into the heart that went through trials, sufferings, darkness, tragedy, loss, and death. The same heart that thirsted for justice, ached in hunger, and longed for the fulfillment of the Lord's promise. This Immaculate Heart needed no purification by the fire of Pentecost, but she received the fire in great ecstasy of spirit, deepening the union of her love with the divine. The coming of the Holy Spirit at Pentecost expanded her motherhood, and the mission in store for her was finally revealed.

"When the day of Pentecost had come, they were all together in one place. And suddenly a sound came from heaven like the rush of a mighty wind, and it filled all the house where they were sitting. And there appeared to them tongues as of fire, distributed and resting on each one of them" (Acts 2:1-3). She was there, often depicted by artists at the center of the community of disciples. When the disciples were filled with the Spirit, they entered more fully into their mission and their priesthood as she did become, is, and always will be the Mother of the Church.

MARY'S VALIANT RECEPTIVITY

She is not just a symbol of the Church but completely intertwined with who and what the Church is. As a creature, she represents humanity as a whole and each of our individual calls to union with God. She is what all human beings were always meant to be: obedient and humble servants of a good and gracious God. She is the bride, the valiant woman of Proverbs more precious than jewels and the heart of her husband turns to her and trusts in her. Christ trusts in her because she is faithful, even unto death and the loss of everything she loves. He trusts in her because she is loyal and walked with him in the dark night of the soul and body, unwavering in faith and ardent love. His Sacred Heart trusts in her immaculate heart because she mirrors him to the world; she is the created one who reflected her creator perfectly to eager lost sheep searching for the truth.

God chose her first. In anticipation of her *fiat* and the redemption of Christ—his death, resurrection, and ascension into heaven—she was cleansed and purified from the beginning. In her childhood, she received God into her heart, and as she grew into a woman, she received him in her womb—the only fitting place for him, the only living tabernacle worthy and able to carry the uncontainable. It is most fitting that the one who could not be contained was contained in the most perfect of women, who took on the flesh, the DNA, the blood, of a human being made to live in perfect union with God's will. Her blood pulsed through his veins, and nothing imperfect touched his divine and human nature. The human and divine natures of Christ were wrapped into one just as a body and soul make up a human being.

Because of this one can see the fittingness that the woman who gave her body and blood, who knew no seed or stain of man, received God within her as she formed his body, his skin, his blood, his eyes, his hands, his feet. Her female body fashioned his male body as she poured herself out in generosity as his mother—responding to the Holy Spirit as God gave the Son to the human race through her pure womb who knew not man. She contained the uncontainable, bore the one who made her, and when he died, she had died inside, entering further, deeper, more fully into his mystery and union with her son.

A MOTHER STRONG AND KIND

Under the holy cross, St. John had looked into the eyes of our mother; in the days of darkness, St. Mary Magdalene had clung to her. Why? Because her hope in the deepest darkness anyone has ever experienced radiated and ignited a spark and calm in all those around her. They clung to their mother, waiting eagerly, wondering why, filled with anxieties, and they met the peace in her eyes, her peaceful surrender. When Christ was raised from the dead, she drew forward in a quiet haste of service once again. And now her service was not so quiet, it was not so hidden any longer. She was entering ever more fully into her mission as Mother of God and preparing for what was coming after the birth of the Church at Pentecost.

It was the work she was prepared for all along, the mission that took her up into heaven and kept her onward. She will not rest until the last day. This mission brought joy, light, anticipation, holy work, a renewal in spirit, a renewed energy, a sense of purpose after Jesus left the earth. But it also brought an ache deep in the recesses of her heart. For just as Christ continued to bear the scars of his wounds in the resurrection, just as he kept them as he ascended into heaven, and just as the scars have never and will never disappear, so she keeps her own wounds.

She keeps the seven piercings of her heart; she keeps her quiet and hidden martyrdom. She suffers still the misunderstanding of others, those who reject her and do not know her. She aches for her children in sin and wails loudly in pain as she, the woman of strength, love, generosity, and angelic kindness whispers gentle promptings to her children: "Come forth, be born again in the living waters of my son, receiving him into your hearts, receive his peace. I will take your hand and guide you!" With this work, the wounds of sorrow remain, but the resurrection, followed by Pentecost, brought a new life.

There was a radiating joy, and that joy spilled over in service to her children. She is a kind mother with the eyes and heart of angelic nature. A calm which calms, a peace which brings peace. Never was she angry with her children. She did not look to her children to condemn them, she never thought, "Their sin has killed my son, and it is just to be angry at such things." No, not once did the Mother of Mercy hold such grumblings within her. Instead, she sees her children with a holy pity, a pity that does not look down upon them but wishes to raise them up.

Like St. Monica praying for St. Augustine's conversion, she saw each spiritual child as her flesh and blood because, in the waters of Baptism, her sons and daughters do become her flesh and blood. Her sons and daughters, as true siblings of Christ, become her own as they look to Holy Mother Church, wrapped in the mantle of the Mother of God, and receive God's mercy.

CHILDREN OF THE VALIANT WOMAN

When Our Lady saw the risen Christ, the Son of God in his glorious and immortal body, the promise had been fulfilled. Born by the waters of Baptism, the sons and daughters of the Church are born by the laboring pains of the woman whose tears water the font and whose Queenship reigns over heaven and earth. Individual members are far from perfect, but in Our Lady, we have the most faithful of brides.

A seed can only sprout from good soil and he, the perfect and most glorious seed, the new tree of life, sprouted from the most fertile and rich soil—the womb of Mary. This is why the early Church was able to recognize Mary and venerate her from the earliest days, knowing that Christ was not only their God, but their brother as well, and so they looked to her as their mother. She was the mother of the Church and the wise woman of whom we read, "She opens her hand to the poor, and reaches out her hands to the needy" (Proverbs 31:20).

It is in the vision of the Mother of God that the disciples were able to see the Church as in a reflection, visibly manifest before them in the Blessed Virgin's perfection, and it was in this moment that she demonstrated to all before her that they too were to be brought up into this mystery, to take on the wounds of Christ, to have Christ's blood pulse within them. The members of the Church are to seek union with him; to receive him in Holy Communion in the state of grace and grow in grace all the more. Mary's daughters are to become "little mothers" to him: reflections of him to the world as daughters, as little women manifesting truth by quiet and hidden lives filled with mission and ignited in God's precise way and timing.

Pentecost lit the flame of mission within the disciples, bearing all the gifts they needed to pivot forward to lead the Church in the war against the world, the flesh, and the devil. They were ignited by the Spirit and were able to live a life in common with the Spirit's true spouse. In their prayer, they were able to call out to her: Oh, holy, and most venerable, and honorable Mother of God. She was, is, and always will be the *Theotokos*, the valiant woman the Old Testament predicted and whispered.

How Might We Imitate Our Lady's Kindness and Strength with All of Her Children?

There is a great temptation these days to not only be harsh with others but to be unimaginably harsh with oneself. And yet if a woman hopes to grow in virtue and hopes to attract others to this growth, kindness mingled with a holy fear of the Lord is the way. Kindness makes waves and can soften even the hardest of hearts. Kindness washes away comparison and seeks the good of the other, it casts off impatience and puts on tenderness and love, it destroys jealousy and replaces it with a sense of awe, of being truly inspired by another. It brings healing where healing is needed, it attracts by way of truth while clinging to love.

KINDNESS AND TRUTH

If a woman has a fiery temperament, she might feel a distaste for kindness and gentleness. Somehow, kindness and gentleness can seem too meek or crippling. Somehow, they can come off as a weakness that places a woman in a vulnerable state of being hurt by others or not being enough or expecting enough as far as growth in virtue is concerned.

In this regard, there are two extremes. The first is that of being too worldly and relativistic. This extreme is a watering down of truth, a pressure to make everyone understand and feel understood, a pressure to please everyone, a pressure to never let another feel sorry or negative about their ways, a pressure for perfection so as not to offend anyone. The other extreme is to try avoiding relativism by being far too blunt, unapologetically and angrily depicting what one believes to be true, leading inevitably to scrupulosity and unrealistic expectations of others.

Both paths hurt the heart and both paths tempt all in different settings and ways.

These extremes are offset by Our Lady's example as a mother to all of her daughters. She shows that true kindness means a woman holds fast to truth without losing her temper. True kindness is courageous and strong while maintaining humility and understanding her weakness. True kindness teaches truth by way of life and living, writing, speaking, and sharing friendship in a spirit of justice and mercy. True kindness and gentleness take on the warrior spirit of the mother of God while maintaining the eyes of a mother upon her children. In the eyes of Our Lady, our mother, we as her daughters find the perfect example of a fiery spirit mingled with kindness.

Our Lady could have turned Magdalene away. In fact, she could have turned all away from her. She had every right to harbor righteous anger at the sight of Calvary. And yet she was not angry. She was receptive and surrendering through all of these trials. Her fiery spirit was alive and well within as her love was set aflame and the swords pierced, and her heart danced. She is the lively, fiery, strong, persevering Queen Mother; passionate for truth, never swaying from it, never apologizing or holding back from God's holy will. Not only was Our Lady not angry with her fellow human beings for their imperfections, but she is able to see far past every deep-rooted sin. She has the power to stir hearts to come back to the truth. She looks with tenderness, love, and gentleness toward all of her children.

THE STRENGTH TO BE KIND

There may be a day, a particularly bad day, in which a woman is quite agitated. Perhaps she feels under the weather, perhaps she is overwhelmed, perhaps she is overtired, withdrawn, or feeling depleted by the demands of life. A friend drops by and rather than questioning her mood gives her an enormous hug and asks her if she would like to sit for tea. This friend, rather than being irritated with the other's bad mood steps in to cheer her and meet her in kindness and a gentle patience.

All women desire more than fair-weather friends and all women can be this kind of friend to one another. This is the kind of friend who is strong, who will support and be there even on the difficult days, the days where one's imperfections and weaknesses rise and are known. True friendship is hard to find but it is the kind that is lasting and quite merciful. It is the kind that bears all things patiently. In those moments where human nature manifests itself, it comes back with support and encouragement. True friendship requires a sense of self-knowledge and the understanding that no woman other than Our Lady is perfect. It knows that therefore one must bear the imperfections of others more patiently and with a deep eagerness and readiness to forgive.

Practically speaking, due to our fallen human nature there are at times wounds which clash in a way that is unfruitful for both people involved. In these more difficult relationships one must set up whatever boundaries she needs to protect her heart; however, she must do so in a charitable way. Part of humility is seeing the truth of a relationship if it is not fruitful or helping her move closer to the Lord. Even in these circumstances when boundaries are needed, she is called to maintain kindness and gentleness to others. This can be done by expressing forgiveness or apologizing, if needed. It may be done by a surrender, silently placing the other upon the altar in an adoration chapel, giving the other to the Lord and asking him to bless them in their journey even though it seems most fitting not to be a part of it any longer. There are circumstances where true charity and kindness is creating this necessary boundary for peace in the midst of fallenness.

Sometimes hard words need to be said. Sometimes truth must be spoken in an unapologetic way. Sometimes irritations arise that are truly angering. This is where a woman's sense of how best to communicate comes into action. To practice being kind, one must be in a situation where it is difficult to be kind. To practice being gentle a woman must be in a place where she does not feel so very gentle. Difficult circumstances are opportunities to overcome ourselves, and to try and try again in failure, bearing patiently with one's own self and others. Being kind as she perceives her own heart and desire for goodness and pouring out that kindness and gentleness in the sight of others is the call of every woman, as any loving mother does for her children, even those most difficult to love.

KINDNESS EVERY DAY

There will be many day-to-day circumstances in which kindness and gentleness can be practiced valiantly and where overcoming self is the most appropriate response. A woman in the work force may find coworkers to be difficult to love, irritating her often, or causing things to be harder in her day. Choosing to smile and say hello every morning will offset the temptation to irritation. A sister or nun may find living within the same community with the same sisters for so long to pose some challenges; moments of difficulties are inevitable in community life. Yet it is precisely in this where her sanctification lies, and grace is poured forth to live with one another and enter into a life within the heart and peace of Christ. When the irritation of a particular sister occurs, she might consider saying something quite kind about that sister and stir up admiration rather than irritation by way of word or note.

A wife and mother may find herself struggling through exhaustion and feeling it difficult to be gentle and kind to her husband or children. This can be offset with simple smiles and slowing life down, rescheduling so as not to over-schedule. She might consider what she can do to refresh herself and how to structure her day in a way that reduces her overwhelm.

Kindness and gentleness need to be at the forefront of a woman's mind, especially on more challenging days: to be extra careful to be gentle, extra careful to be kind, and extra prudent with words. And when she inevitably is unkind, too harsh, or too blunt she might make a call to Our Lady—a quick call, "Mother be my mother now," or "Mother, teach me holy motherhood," or "Mother, teach me to be your daughter"—and start fresh and renew. In seeing this in herself she is reminded to be quickly forgiving of others' bad days, difficult seasons, weak moments, as well.

There are always temptations in the opposite direction, tugs on the heart to not be what one ought to be, little whispers of comparison, jealousy, harshness, or detraction of others. There is a reason the devil tempts women to dislike and hurt one another. There is a reason why he tempts them to anger, harshness, and to pride. It is precisely in this way that he hopes women will lose their kind and gentle nature.

That gentle and kind nature of woman is powerful and intrinsically tied to her maternal instinct. It is by and through gentleness that the little ones are attracted to truth. Harshness will never win others over in love; it may cause fear perhaps, but not love. This movement in gentle nature is needed now more than ever for the conversion of the world; for the conversion of sinners; for the conversion that takes place every day within oneself. Our Lady, our Mother, the Mother of the Church, guides our way.

CHAPTER 11

Clothed in the Son

Imitating Mary's Heavenly Wisdom as a Beautiful Woman

Wisdom cannot be bought; it cannot be gained through anything but grace and life experience. It is the woman who has suffered, who has sacrificed, who has given all for the sake of others who finds herself built up in character. Our Lady, so closely connected to the feminine aspects of wisdom, embodied the prudence of a humble and seasoned mother. In her perfect wisdom and beauty, shining as the Queen of Heaven, she draws us to herself as beloved daughters. In the beauty of her heart, we find our wisdom and beauty.

Mary, the Faithful Mother

When Christ ascended into heaven Mary's heart continued to yearn for her son. She found solace in the early years within the liturgy of the budding Church. She took part in it and received him: body, blood, soul, and divinity within the holy Eucharist, offered from the hands of her spiritual sons, the apostles, the priests and bishops of the early Church who spent the years leading the flock and seeking the conversion of the nations.

In her quiet and humble way, she spoke the truths of those secret moments in Bethlehem, of her flight into Egypt, and the loss of the child Jesus in the Temple. She was able to share the moments she was troubled, the moments she was amazed, the moments of sorrow, and the moments of joy. Yes, all of these things she whispered into the ears of the apostles, and they wrote them down. For the early Church—and for the universal Church until the end of time—the Word of God in Scripture owes much of the Gospel narrative to her.

THE BEAUTY OF MARY

The early Church was well aware she was set apart, the queen and mother of the living, and they depicted her holiness in icons showing her maternal role in salvation history. How fitting it is that the uncontainable God chose a woman who, from the beginning, maintained purity of heart, mind, soul, and body. How fitting that her womb was untouched by man past, present, and future, preserving her purity and love entirely in God. How fitting God created a most beautiful and perfect creature who captured the goodness of himself, made in his image and mirrored him to the world. God crowned Our Lady with many stars; she is the queen of his heart, the woman untarnished, the New Eve, and the Mother of all of his chosen ones.

She proved herself repeatedly amongst daily trials and struggles. She proved herself in the sweeping, the cooking, the cleaning and in the dishes and dusting, the gardening and mending. She proved herself in faithfulness in loss, in states of human anxiety, in darkness and dryness, in desert and rain. The peak of the proof of love was her complete and utter surrender at the foot of the holy cross, where her heart was pierced with the arrows of divine love and she suffered for his sake, for God's sake, for our sake. There she bore fruit in death and labored for her many children.

Her body was completely in tune with her soul's disposition, living out the covenant love of the Scriptures as a woman who never failed in faithfulness, fully pleasing God and being most loved by God. Her beauty was pleasing to the Lord, and he delighted in her. She captured the essence of modesty, humility, simplicity, surrender. She is the woman of receptivity, willing to suffer in sacrificial surrender, and filled with unending and exuberant joy. She is the woman of deep love, tenderness, kindness, and strength. She is the woman of fire and vibrance, bravery and courage.

She radiated all that was truly beautiful in the cosmos, and in woman. She was the gift to the New Adam, in whom he took such great delight, filled with delight at the glory of the beauty with which he had fashioned her. Is it not fitting to think most of her beauty in her old age, in her wisdom and holiness, in her faithfulness, in her suffering? This was the woman willing to sacrifice everything for the sake of love, willing to suffer and die a martyr's death.

QUEEN OF HEAVEN

Her whispers of comforts among the new disciples, the converted pagans, the apostles themselves lasted many years, and in her old age, her wisdom and beauty shone bright. Our Lady aged as any other creature, yet she aged in elegance and simplicity, yearning and longing for her heavenly home. And when she lay on her deathbed, they came.

Anyone who could come came to be with the holy Mother of God; to sing psalms, to remember her presence, to feel her peace, to experience her beauty, to be witness to this living embodiment of holiness.

Tradition holds that death took this beautiful one. It was a fitting end for the one who would do anything to follow in the footsteps of her son to pass through the portals of death before the crowning of her glory. Christ came to her as he promised he would. Her soul was reunited to her body and her body was raised and assumed into heaven, luminous and new. She was crowned the Queen of Heaven and the Queen of Earth, her earthly tears and labor shining bright in the crown with many stars.

She took her place alongside the archangel Michael, who had cast the demons out of heaven before Eden had even been established. St. Michael had proclaimed his service to God for all eternity, fulfilling that promise in every act of his being as a purely spiritual creature.

Our Lady saw deep into this angel's being, finding eternal friendship in St. Michael. She, the little maiden, the girl with the *fiat* that radiated into the whole of her life, crushed the head of Satan, guarding her heart from him entirely. She was untouched by evil in her soul, the bride become mother yet remaining a virgin, and given to God. She is the ultimate soldier for Christ—the Queen-Mother, the warrior queen who has conquered the world, the flesh, and the devil.

The external evils of life, the suffering and death, the torments and miseries, all were nothing in comparison to the vision before her of her glorified son, the King of the Universe, the Second Person of the most Holy Trinity, the God-Man of contradiction. She knelt down before her king, and he took her face in his hands and said, "My Queen. My faithful one. My Beloved Mother, My Sister, My Bride." The angels bow down before their queen, and for generation upon generation her children call her blessed.

A WISE MOTHER FOR HER CHILDREN

Behold your queen ... behold your mother: "And a great sign appeared in heaven, a woman clothed with the sun, with the moon under her feet, and on her head a crown of twelve stars; she was with child and she cried out in her pangs of birth, in anguish for delivery" (Revelation 12:1-2).

From that moment of her crowning in heaven, Mary continues in the pangs of spiritual childbirth, in a mother's state of ongoing holy anxiety with a wish for her children to do what is good for themselves, to be holy, to give their lives entirely to Christ. She does this as a mirror—a mirror reflecting the beauty of her son. She is the woman whose eyes radiate peace and draw others into the truths of Christ.

She was a widow for every widow on earth, suffering the loss of the one she loved. She lost her child for every woman on earth who has ever buried her own children. She is a virgin for every woman on earth vowing her whole life to the Church as one of Christ's holy brides. She is a mother for every mother on earth who rocks her baby to sleep, guiding, teaching, listening, and hoping for her children's sanctity. She is a sign of contradiction in complete imitation of her son: virgin and mother, bride and servant to all, the Mother of the Living.

She is the faithful creature who walked the steps of earth without faltering as the consistent and perfect consolation to her only begotten son. In her absence, the early Church meditated upon her life as she had once pondered the mysteries of Christ's life. They humbled themselves, they sacrificed, they died, they followed the road to the holy cross in imitation of their king and their queen. They saw in the eyes of Mary comfort in the pains of life, perseverance in the sight of trial, and beauty in the eyes of their mother.

True beauty is found in the eyes of the wise woman, for it is only she who radiates the beauty which is entirely unfading. Our Lady, the beautiful one, is Lady Wisdom, reflecting the heart of divine wisdom:

> Wisdom is radiant and unfading,
>
> and she is easily discerned by those who love her,
>
> and is found by those who seek her.
>
> She hastens to make herself known to those who desire her.
>
> He who rises early to seek her will have no difficulty,
>
> for he will find her sitting at his gates.
>
> To fix one's thought on her is perfect understanding,
>
> and he who is vigilant on her account will soon be free from care,
>
> because she goes about seeking those worthy of her,
>
> and she graciously appears to them in their paths,
>
> and meets them in every thought. (Wisdom 6:12-16)

She is the one holding fast to all facets of all things true without fail, without a second thought to misunderstandings, or the opinions of others. "The road of the cross is not comfortable," she proclaims, "but this is the way, and I am the hand that will guide you, as a tender mother along the road. I will keep you safe and protected in the shadow of my mantle, I will never leave your side, and when you call on me at your death I will be there ready to lead you through the gate to my divine son for all of eternity in which you will rest in the glory of the Beatific Vision for your own glorified body to be returned. I will not rest, and I will labor, and I will cry out in pain for the sake of all my children, as I wish all of them to turn away from sin and come home to my one and only son, the Lord Jesus Christ."

"The cross is a paradox, and the world does not understand it. The world runs from suffering, but you, my daughter, know better. You know that suffering is made beautiful when united to the holy cross and that anything given to my son will be used to purify your own soul and draw others into grace. I will never leave my children to be unattended; I will always answer your call when you beckon me. I will, from heaven, continue to labor and give birth to my spiritual sons and daughters, to wrap them in my mantle, and encourage them on their journey. You are safe on this journey with me, for I am your mother."

How Might We Grow in Heavenly Wisdom and Reflect True Beauty to the World?

The world tells women that beauty fades, but the beauty of the soul never does. Human beings are composed of both body and soul, and the holier a woman becomes the more beauty she radiates, the more timeless she is, and the more she reflects God's love into a fallen world. In this timeless beauty, the wisdom of woman is discovered and shared.

CALLED TO BE A QUEEN

The woman, the final creature brought forth in Genesis, is the crowned jewel of the cosmos. Adam delighted in Eve. Her companionship, friendship, and physical beauty he beheld with such awe and admiration. "This at last is bone of my bones and flesh of my flesh; she shall be called Woman, because she was taken out of Man" (Genesis 2:23). He cherished her in the wholeness of her nature, a creature like unto himself and yet complimentary in body and soul. Her body is soft and nurturing, ready to receive and bear life into the world. Her body is made with one of the greatest capacities of the human race: the power to receive and grow new life, a sacred soil within her that blossoms forth with the touch of the God who brings a soul into being with an immortal destiny, living on for all eternity.

Yes, this is the greatest gift given to woman, the privilege and height of a woman's human experience: to create another human being, to foster life, to form and guide and lead that little soul into adulthood to know, love and serve God. There is something particularly elevated about the call to spiritual motherhood. The Tradition of the Church holds the supremacy of choosing to remain a virgin by sacrificing the natural desire for parenthood. A religious sister becomes the bride of Christ and points the whole world beyond herself to a heavenly reality. So too the bride who marries and yet finds herself incapable of conceiving a child, though she is not called to give herself to Christ in the same way as the religious, she too can participate in this elevated call to spiritual motherhood. The pain and suffering she receives as a piercing of her own heart will bear life into the world for her spiritual children.

Her spiritual children will go before her into life, in her family, in her friends, in her community. She will foster and bring life to them with the assistance of God's grace, and as is so often the case she will also have spiritual children unknown to her, brought forth as the fruit of her suffering. When she offers her heartache for a natural child to Christ on the holy cross, she unites this deep-rooted pain to Christ's own Sacred Heart, and by this offering, souls can be saved.

Her surrender in her sigh of suffering as a wound to the heart is fashioned into something beautiful; it may take time, patience, and perseverance through the trial, but it is in the intensities of all of the emotions she feels that Christ meets her and loves her through each moment. Her heart suffering may be deep and lasting, but she can take solace in being offered a calling so near to the cross, close enough to receive a kiss from Christ.

Motherhood is the crown of woman, and each little woman is called to be a little mother, and each little mother is called to be Christ's little queen, and each little queen is called to be crowned and clothed in virtue, brought into the mystery of God's love by and through her particular mission on earth.

THE WISDOM OF LOVE

The mission of every individual woman will necessarily look different, for each personality is unique, and each temperament will manifest itself in particular gifts and challenges. In addition, each human being has a particular upbringing, exposures, joys, sorrows, traumas, pains, and experiences in life that make up who one is. The wise woman will understand this and gently, in her own motherhood, guide others along just as Our Lady guides her along.

She will see fallen human nature and have pity for those deep in sin, wishing to draw them out of it. In the sight of disquiet, anxiety, pain, and fear, she will be a giver of peace, calm, courage, and strength and will be a resting place for tired and weary souls. When a friend calls, she will listen. When a family member is in need of service, she will serve. When a toddler beckons, she will come. When a husband is weary in his work, she will be his resting place.

Old age will not bring bitterness, anger, and pain. Rather, the virtuous woman will live into her old age with joy, simplicity, and wisdom, content in her peace and faithfulness to God. She will look back over her life experience and share her wisdom with those in their youth, assisting them along their journey to heaven. The wise woman will, in a sense, lose herself in love.

She does not lose who she is as a daughter of God, her individual personality and gifts. No. These gifts—this personality—is exactly what God has in mind for her and the qualities she needs to fulfill her particular calling.

It is the wise woman who knows when to speak and when to be silent. It is the wise woman who acts in humility rather than pride. It is the wise woman who works diligently with her hands, shedding away all that is ugly and embracing all that is authentic and beautiful. The greater part of wisdom in this regard is operating with an understanding of the fallen nature that one inhabits, and that no other woman besides Our Lady is perfect.

Perfection in Christ is a noble thing to seek, but the wise woman will not become a slave to the impossible. She will simultaneously except her weaknesses, failings, and sinfulness in great acts of humility while remaining driven to grow, shed, and put off the old woman to become a woman of Christ. She will see herself in an ever-growing, ever-changing manner, never settling for where she is and yet contently accepting the reality of her own frailties.

TRUE BEAUTY

Wisdom and beauty go hand in hand. The wise woman will be clothed in the Son, again and again, meeting him with the lived-in, frayed, and dirty robes Magdalene once bore and allowing Christ to wash her clean and clothe her in himself. This new cloth—white and pure, red in suffering, blue in the fullness of humanity, green with life, purple with royalty as a daughter of God—will shimmer like gold before the world. The ever-growing reality of holiness will manifest through her glistening eyes mirroring beauty and peace to the world around her.

The beauty of woman is simple, it is modest, it is humble, and it is fostered by a disciplined prayer life steeped in the sacraments. Without Christ, beauty does in fact fade; sin manifests itself and bears bad fruit and an unbearable odor. On the other hand, true beauty never fades. It radiates in the joy of the saints; the glistening eyes of virtue and fragrance of all that is good. This is the type of glow one experiences at the sight of a sister, nun, or consecrated virgin who has in grace given the whole of her life to Christ. It is the kind of beauty seen in the bride on her wedding day as she beholds her beloved groom, and the kind of beauty seen in the postpartum mother holding her beloved newborn child. Each of these moments reflects something of the Eternal; something good and true and beautiful. The virtuous woman is the beautiful woman.

KNOWING WHO WE ARE

To faithfully practice this, to grow in virtue and become a wise woman of beauty, we must return to the foundation of Our Lady's essence: humility. To be humble before the Lord is to be wise, and with humility as the cornerstone growth in holiness will follow.

So often human nature is inclined to take control, to decide just how best to use one's gifts and create an idea of what it means to flourish in society based on cultural norms and opinions. The woman of wisdom will take each significant life decision to deep prayer. She will consider practically what each decision entails and the paths set before her. She will consider whether an action is reasonable and good or whether it goes against reason and Church teaching. She will also consider the more difficult decisions—the kind of decisions where both options are good, and she will pray and use her intellect and goodwill to decide which path to take. Then she will take that path with a holy confidence.

A head held high in holy confidence is that of a woman who boasts in God and not herself. She will seek to know God's way and study the Scriptures and the truths of Holy Mother Church. She will find her identity in the Word, in Christ, and draw near to Our Lady. She will take Our Lady as Christ did, as her very own mother.

How could an imperfect woman imitate the most perfect woman of all? Our Lady, shining as Queen of Heaven, her eyes filled with the beauty of perfect wisdom, draws each woman to herself. She bears them into the world as her daughters of virtue, and goodness, daughters who capture the timeless beauty of the saints. She guides her daughters to be the kind of women who radiate the light of Christ and who reflect (as a mirror to the world) the love of God that brings warm love to a cool room, serves others willingly, works diligently, and is dutiful in her willingness to sacrifice for a greater good. None of these things can be accomplished without God. It is in his grace where the impossible is made possible. He has proved it to his daughters over and over again that a life given to him is a life that flourishes.

CHAPTER 12

Our Sweetness and Our Hope

Imitating the Perfect Woman as an Imperfect Woman

In the mess of the day-to-day, there are many failings and faults on account of weakness, but the good God is ever more attracted to his little daughters and desires to wash them clean and move them forward. Likewise, his mother is particularly tender as she has lived the most fully human life that has ever been lived, and thus is able to empathize and relate to her children even more than could possibly be imagined.

She is there to guide us, help us, protect us, nurture us, and teach us to beg for hearts of flesh, hearts that have the capacity to feel and experience the greatest joy and the greatest sorrows with trust and unwavering hope in the eternal Father's plan. When we feel lost, frail, weak, or tempted, she is there as a loving mother ready to answer her daughter's call. She turns away no one who asks this assistance from her, for she does not have the heart to resist.

MOTHER OF MERCY

"Mother, teach me to be your daughter." I hope this little prayer has drawn you in—as it did me—to more fully understand the gentleness of our Mother in heaven, who wants nothing more than to see us happy and home at the end of our earthly pilgrimage. She is our advocate and our hope, the help of all Christians, the distributor of graces and the mother of mercy toward all sinners. She will never leave or abandon us, never hurt or perplex us, never lead us to despair or temptation. She is the patient mother who bears our sinfulness with tender love, drawing us ever nearer to her son the more we draw near to her. She is the mother of mercy.

Our Lady never sinned. She never had to deal with marital infidelity, or with a child who has fallen away from the Faith, or with the shame of her own failures, but I will tell you something, dear ones, and this time I will proclaim it from the rooftops as long as I shall live: Our Lady carried in her heart the burden of our sins, and in imitation of her son was, is, and always will be a mother of mercy.

Our Lady had a faithful child on earth, but her spiritual children constantly rebel, cry out, panic, struggle, and prove themselves impatient, and yet she meets all of those struggles with tenderness and serenity. Our Lady knew no sin, but she sees the sins of her children and cries for us tears of truth and justice and compassion, wishing to draw us back into the graces of her son through Holy Mother Church and the reception of the sacraments, especially Reconciliation and the Holy Eucharist.

Our Lady is the tender Mother who leads us to her Son. She is the Queen whom we admire and aspire to be like out of admiration for her beauty, goodness, kindness, and virtue. She is the woman who takes her daughter's hand and places it into her son's, and as she stands between daughter and son, she presses her forehead against her daughter's forehead and holds her cheek in the palm of her hand as if to say:

"My little daughter, how I love you and how I desire you to see yourself as you truly are: you are my son's daughter … sister … bride. You are called to stand beside him in the days that you only see a dungeon as well as those in which you rejoice in victory in the days of glistening light. You are not alone. I am here for you, as a tender mother for you to lean on, to rely on. I will always hear your call and beckoning, and I promise to come to your aid. I am the "M" written on your heart, the mother who will kneel next to you at the cross.

"Receive the healing I have in store for you. Bear the wounds my son has asked you to bear in imitation of him as he says, 'bear my wounds!' Know my motherhood and my goodness and receive my loving friendship. It does not matter how far away or how wretched you feel; it is good to remain humble, to know your weaknesses, and to stay little. This is the way of true receptivity that will draw down grace upon grace into the valley of your soul. I will assist you and wipe your face clean in this hidden chamber. I will encourage you to receive the sacraments and to receive my son's constant forgiveness, justice, and mercy. I will assist you in all seasons in life and help you discern what it is God is asking of you.

"I want you to know who you are, dear daughter. I want you to know who you were made to be as woman that you might live out God's plan for your life—to be the most woman you can be. I want you to seek a virtuous life with your whole heart while accepting your frailty and weakness. You will grow. You will change. You will be part of authoring your own beautiful love story between you and my son. I want you to pray unceasingly, especially for the faith to know the power of your prayers, your fasts, and your mortifications for the sake of the kingdom."

"MOTHER, TEACH ME TO BE YOUR DAUGHTER"

Yes, Our Lady says all of these things to her little daughters, inspiring those who aspire to be like her. She is not a goddess, nor an unapproachable and untouchable, nor is she puffed up with pride and demanding to be worshipped. She is the humble queen, the little maiden kept pure from the moment of her conception in her mother's womb into eternity. She knows that is precisely who she is. She is the lowly asked to rise up. She is the yes to our no. She is the faithful to the unfaithful and she wishes to represent her daughters as holy mother Church. She is the creature who calls all creatures to give God all his due and to love him unceasingly. She is woman fully alive.

We will face mountains, valleys, and deserts, and yet ultimately, we are meant to be drawn forth into the fires of divine love to be purified in the abode of suffering, intimately united to Christ by grace. The saints have a way of making suffering look light and easy, beautiful, and even inspiring. One need only look at the narratives that surround the martyr's call or the virgin's sacrifice and we might note this. This is no natural power, for it is only through the power of God and the presence of Christ within them that they are able to bear him once again to the world, in imitation of Mary.

Those who will succeed will have the hand of Our Lady holding theirs, with her mantle of protection surrounding them. The beautiful truth is that no one is too lost to receive the help of this mother, no one is too far away to make this ascent, no one is unworthy of her merciful and maternal heart.

SMALL STEPS

To enter most fully into God's storytelling, we must strive to remain faithful to the duty of the present moment, imitating Our Lady's *fiat* with each step forward. She shows us that it is precisely our faithfulness in the small tasks, in the hidden moments and acts of service we surrender each day, that sanctify us when done in the spirit of love. The small moments will lead to greater faithfulness, and so when a storm threatens to shake us and the crosses of life feel far too heavy, we can find consolation in our mother's example of exceeding faithfulness and wisdom in such circumstances. This fidelity, however, will only grow and be manifest when grounded in a faithful prayer life, deep humility, and ardent love—all of which Our Lady encompasses perfectly, and all of which she desires to teach us, as her daughters.

We might accept our crosses, forgive wrongs quickly, and hand over our lives to Christ fully and completely as best we know how. We might increase our prayer, dedicate ourselves to a daily Rosary, and consecrate ourselves and our families to Jesus Christ through Our Lady as the Ark of the New Covenant who will protect us through storms both present and to come.

We can imitate her ways by pondering them in our own hearts. We can take one virtue every week and have it at the forefront of our minds to practice and pray with. She is not asking us to be perfect; she is asking us to try our very best and let her son manage the rest as he pours grace into our hearts. She is inviting us on an adventure of everlasting love, holiness, goodness, and true joy.

The way of perfection is simple: it is to love, to remain little, to remain humble, to know ourselves and persevere in the path of holiness, a path lined with roses and thorns; to turn outside of ourselves and seek with the fullness of our hearts the pearl of great price.

Our Mother will help us in our struggle. She may be meek, gentle, and mild, but Our Lady is also the strongest woman that ever lived. She faced suffering heroically and proves to us that all suffering united to the holy cross is sanctifying and will save souls. Nothing, no life, no moment goes to waste when given to Our Lord Jesus Christ the king, the beloved of our souls, our brother and our God.

I hope this book inspires each of us to be women who bear life into the world, who radiate beauty, who spread goodness far and wide, and rejoice in the truth in all seasons, in every suffering, in each joy, and in all circumstances. I hope that we embrace our God-given dignity and the privilege of being a woman.[4]

Who am I? Who are you? Who are we? We are pilgrims on earth making our way to the promised land—sailing to the final destination with a lighthouse guiding our way. We are daughters of a God who loves us profoundly, so much so that he has gifted us with the most beautiful and perfect of mothers. You are a daughter of Mary, and she loves you very much.

Christ chooses who he wills: the weak, the tired, the weary, the suffering, the humble, the little, and he washes them clean, white as snow. Our

Mother Mary knows Jesus chooses you, too. And so this Woman of all women will not rest until she sees her sons and daughters home in heaven with vocations perfected, missions fulfilled, and the beatific vision before their eyes. Be the most woman you can be.

A Parable: Clothed in Mary

Let me tell you a parable.

There was once a little woman outside the gates of a great kingdom lying flat on her face prostrate, her face pushed deep into the soil. She was a beggar thin from lack of nourishment, rags for clothes hung off her body and dirt lay thick upon her face. Her entire figure, in fact, was stained with filth—her hands, her ears, her nostrils, the whole of her body and garments. She was all that is wretched and disfigured. In a deep moment of humiliation, a man who had hidden himself up to this point approached her kindly,

The man said, "What do you want? Would you like to speak with the King?"

She responded, "I cannot go in, I am too dirty. Will you tell him something for me?" She thought he was the guard or the gatekeeper, perhaps.

The man said, "What would you like me to tell him for you?"

She responded with a simple request, "Tell him that I love him."

The man replied, "Get up little one, and come with me."

The woman lay still, face in the ground, hands outstretched in prostration, feeling too wretched to even lift her face. He bent down and lifted her chin and looked into her eyes. He took her hands and said, "Daughter, rise up."

So the woman rose and followed him through the gates to an inner chamber deep within the castle. He brought her into the innermost room where stood a beautiful clawfoot tub, a library of books of wisdom that lined the walls from floor to ceiling, a bed in which to rest, and one wall completely covered by a curtain. It was a marvelous apartment, but before she could even notice, the man had disappeared. He had left her, however, in the care of a maid to care for her as women do. The maiden was fair and very kind, and she was gentle with the dirty little woman whom she met with a kind eye, a silent smile, and a careful hand. First, her face was washed, and then her ears, her nose, her mouth, her body, and finally she was stripped of her clothing. She felt so exposed in this manner and the process was humiliating, but she trusted that she had been left in good hands, and she hoped that perhaps this was the way to appear before the king. One must be clothed properly, she surmised.

In the process of her cleansing, she found she could see with greater clarity, and that she could smell and hear more vividly. A soft cloth went over her whole body, while her beggar's clothes turned to ash in the fireplace. Now clothed in a white garment, she had been made clean. Over this white garment lay two strips of gold: one lying over her left shoulder that reached over to the right, and the other on the right shoulder reaching over to the left. In the center of these two golden strips, which gave the appearance of a cross etched across her body, she saw the letter M stitched in blue across her heart.

When she turned all the way around and looked into the mirror, she gazed upon her reflection clearly for the first time. Her face was radiant, her skin taut with youth, her eyes shone bright as stars, her nails clear and clean, and her body gleamed as she had never seen it before. She stared at her image in the mirror, awed at the beauty in the glass. As she noticed the freckles on her cheeks for the first time (illuminated by the contrast with her simple white garment, highlighted by the details of the golden strips across her chest), she heard a knock upon the door, and a voice that asked permission to enter.

She opened the door and once again the same guard stepped forth. Holding his hands out, he asked, "Which would you have?" There before her were two different crowns with which to meet the king: an exquisitely wrought circlet (clearly meant for royalty), and a crudely fashioned crown of thick vine and thorns. She took the crown of thorns into her hands and felt them prick the palms of her hands. She noticed him gazing deep into her eyes, almost as if he could see through her, and she felt he knew her thoughts exactly. Reaching out his hand he took the crown back and presented both to her again. He asked her, "Which do you choose?" Once again, she took the crown of thorns. He took the crown a third time and again he asked, only to see the woman chose the crown of thorns once more.

He stepped closer to her, so close that she could see her reflection in his eyes, and she saw herself, but this time she looked strikingly similar to him—she had not been transfigured as much as she merely seemed to resemble him in his wounds, wounds that she had not noticed before. Her face began to sweat and her heart began to bleed, and she found that she looked like this guard who had suddenly appeared to be suffering deeply, revealing to her what he looked like in the moments that he had been bruised, disfigured, and broken. She looked up into his face, strangely weary as she heard him speak: "Do you know who I am?"

"Yes," she said, for it was true, she had recognized his true identity, "You are my beloved."

He went on. "You see yourself as this wretched little girl," he continued, "a beggar outside the gate, dirty, broken, and miserable. This is not quite the truth. This is how I see you, my daughter, my sister, my bride. Shall I show you?"

As if thrust from the confines of her own body, the girl beheld herself standing in front of him, clothed in an ivory wedding dress that spread across the floor like a river, stitched from the finest lace and with long sleeves ornamented with beautiful lace details. The rosary she had clasped in her hand had been changed into a sword, she wore a scapular as a shield, and a crown lay upon her head, glistening with jewels and illuminated by a mysterious light. It was a crown for a queen, set with pearls and rubies round about, prepared with empty settings as if waiting to be decked with even more precious stones over time.

The Lord spoke to her, for it was him indeed: "My little queen, what is it you desire?"

She said, "I want you."

His smile was brilliant as he answered, "Look at your rosary. Do you see how beautiful the cross is? Be reminded of that beauty every time you look at it. My cross is beautiful." He then led her deeper into the hidden and private chambers of the castle where he taught her various things from the books of wisdom that lined the walls. He spoke intimately with her there and showed her gardens which though beautiful needed a tremendous amount of constant work to keep up.

The little woman often found herself lying prostrate on her face, this time not outside the gate but in this interior castle which seemed to shift and change unexpectedly; sometimes it seemed as she sat in a dungeon, that is, within a certain darkness or a dimly lit room that at times felt uncomfortable, but every so often she would be bathed in light and the room changed into a marvelous ballroom in which she danced, rejoiced, laughed, and marveled. In this ballroom she would find her greatest joy, meeting her beloved Jesus in the most inner chamber where they spoke intimately and visiting with the Queen Mother who demonstrated a great and tender love for the woman she now saw as her daughter. It was an ever-growing, ever-changing journey of love, of being made clean, of failing, and cleaning up again; but through it all the woman persevered, and over time her garments became less and less tarnished, and though her heart ached her face was always damp with the sweat of labor and perseverance.

One day, when the inner room had grown bright with light and driven away her suffering, the Queen entered the chamber with her son. The Queen took the woman's hand and placed it into Jesus' hand, setting a ring upon her finger. The Queen Mother stood between them drawing the girl closer to her son, who looked yearningly upon her, desiring her life, her beauty, her strength, and her weakness—all of her for the sake of what she was to become. In that moment, she felt certain he would turn away at the sight of her, knowing who she truly was, a beggar from the beginning.

In the time that she had been left in the inner parts of the castle, she had often fashioned prisons for herself and had dirtied the castle often. Again and again, she found herself flat on the ground, humiliated, but in that practice of humility her tears and exasperation for her imperfections turned into laughter. "Yes! I am small! Yes, I am imperfect! And yes, I am very much loved!" Not cheaply, not in a shallow manner, not even a love rooted in the passions of the body. This love was that which lasts through great earthquakes and torrents of the sea, the love that is stronger than death, and which in turn leads to a manner of death itself—a love that draws the lover outside of herself into something so much more. This self-sacrificing love declares itself time and time again by meeting the beloved in their most vulnerable moments. This is the love of the cross, and she decided forever more to cling to it, next to the Queen Mother beside her.

A POEM
"Mother, Teach Me to Be Your Daughter"

Mother, teach me to be your daughter.

Who am I but a servant unworthy?

The little one who no one knew,

Who hid away in the upper room, full of hope and drained by life?

The little mother, tired and unmoved

You swooped me up and washed away,

Gently and tenderly removing the unmoved

Surgical procedures met with tears,

A death, or two and aches unspoken of

My lantern kept lit, deep into the night

The misery

The darkness

The humiliation

The tears

The oil lamp stirred and danced until a Heart came

And showed me how to dance

And so I danced with this Heart

And two became one

Forever changed

Renewed

Refreshed

Undone

A chalice with an overflowing cup

Of choicest wine, met and brought forth
by the lips and request of a Mother

Who brought me to drink the blood red wine

To the wedding feast

Where we danced

And two became one

The toil continues on; the land must be tilled

The roses only bloom in the noonday sun

When the gardener does her part.

With love,
a little mother

Discussion Questions

CHAPTER 1

MOTHER, TEACH ME TO BE YOUR DAUGHTER: EMBARKING ON THE JOURNEY

1. What are some characteristics I attribute to the Blessed Mother? How can each person, with her own temperament and personality, relate to her?

2. What does it mean for me to be Mary's daughter? How does that disposition change my approach when asking for her help and intercession?

3. In what ways is the world wounded in its idea of the maternal woman? How might I find healing in my understanding of motherhood in Mary?

4. What does Mary's *fiat* mean for me on my own journey in holiness? How can she inspire me by her radical "yes" to God?

5. What am I hoping to receive by the end of this book?

CHAPTER 2

FIAT IN EACH MOMENT: IMITATING MARY'S HUMILITY AS A RECEPTIVE WOMAN

1. How does being humbled, stripped bare, and emptied help me receive Christ more fully?

2. As a woman, I have a natural gift for receptivity. How does this gift manifest itself spiritually, emotionally, and tangibly in my life?

3. Where am I in my own spiritual journey? Is it dry, is it dark, is it joyful, is it abundant, is it impoverished, is it a time of reception?

4. How can I, like the Blessed Mother and St. Elizabeth, bring Christ into my relationships and conversations?

5. How can I find joy in my daily life and duties?

CHAPTER 3

THE HIDDEN ONE: IMITATING MARY'S LIVELY FAITH AS A MATERNAL WOMAN

1. What does it mean to live in the world and yet remain hidden? What does this look like in my particular state in life?

2. In what ways does "hiddenness" protect my heart from the world?

3. How does Mary transcend the mundane and ordinary work in her quiet life in Nazareth?

4. How might I live out radical faith in my particular season spiritually? What relation does this have to a lively faith and trust in God?

5. Mary was present to each moment. How can I be inspired by this presence and enter more fully into the duty of the moment in front of me?

CHAPTER 4

WISDOM POURED FORTH: IMITATING MARY'S OBEDIENCE AS A DISCERNING WOMAN

1. How can I live the beauty of virtuous obedience? What does it look like in my state of life?

2. What are some challenges associated with submission and obedience?

3. How can Mary inspire me in radical obedience to God's will? In what ways can I imitate her unshakable trust?

4. What are practical exercises I might do to become a more discerning woman? How can I more peacefully make significant decisions in my life?

5. In what ways can I foster a home in my heart for Jesus to rest?

CHAPTER 5

THEY HAVE NO WINE: IMITATING MARY'S UNCEASING PRAYER AS A PERSEVERING WOMAN

1. What does living out active service and a contemplative spirit look like? How can I be inspired by Mary's ability to live out both fully? Are there seasons I am called to one more than the other?

2. What prayers am I drawn to say daily? What prayers would I like to add to my prayer routine? How might I keep a spirit of prayer throughout the whole of my day?

3. The holier I become, the more capacity for sorrows and joys I will have—in what way is this connected to a radical ability to love?

4. How can I seek Christ with my whole heart when I am dry, when I am walking in spiritual darkness, or when Christ feels far away?

5. How can I find encouragement in my prayer life? What are ways I can encourage others?

CHAPTER 6

DO WHATEVER HE TELLS YOU: IMITATING MARY'S SELF-DENIAL AS A SELF-SACRIFICIAL WOMAN

1. What does it mean to have a "pondering" heart? How might I practice this pondering in my daily life?

2. To cultivate spiritual blossoms, I must begin in the soil, making sure it is rich. How might I dig deep and cultivate this soil of my heart? What does this metaphor mean?

3. Are all the desires in my heart fulfilled or do I need to undergo a purification before they might be fulfilled? How might I meet the desires of my heart with unfailing hope? How might I respond with a spirit of surrender to God's perfect will, in imitation of Mary?

4. Why is suffering united to Christ redemptive? In what ways is this part of my "training" on the road to holiness?

5. What does self-sacrificial love look like in my state of life? Where am I meant to pour out more of myself, and in what areas do I need to give myself more grace and kindness in my journey?

CHAPTER 7
MATER DOLOROSA: IMITATING MARY'S PURITY AS A BRIDAL WOMAN

1. Mary is a daughter of God, a sister, a mother, a bride, and a queen. What title am I currently most drawn to and why?

2. What does it mean to walk with Christ in his Passion faithfully? How can Mary inspire me in greater faithfulness during trials?

3. What is the benefit of surrendering to God? Will this make me happy, and if so, how?

4. How can we comfort others who are suffering? In what ways can I serve others and offer support? How is this living out a "Marian spirit"?

5. What is the connection between having a receptive heart and experiencing God's mercy?

CHAPTER 8

WOUNDED BY LOVE: IMITATING MARY'S ARDENT LOVE AS A SENSITIVE WOMAN

1. What does it mean to be "wounded by love"? How does this relate to the spiritual life?

2. Why do love and responsibility go hand in hand? How does this differ from a worldly approach to love?

3. What responsibilities do I have in my current state of life? How can I fuel those duties with more love and joy?

4. How can Mary inspire me to preserve a heart of flesh, a heart that feels, a heart that maintains a certain sensitivity? How can she help me avoid hardening at the sight of suffering? How might I maintain a certain delicacy in my womanhood in imitation of Mary?

5. In what ways does suffering draw me intimately closer to Christ and the Blessed Mother?

CHAPTER 9

MY DAUGHTER, I LOVE YOU: IMITATING MARY'S PATIENCE AS A NURTURING WOMAN

1. In what ways does St. Mary Magdalene represent all women at the foot of the cross? How does she inspire me to follow Mary to Calvary?

2. Why is it brave to receive God's mercy? Why is this act so pertinent to spiritual growth?

3. Mary wishes to live out her motherhood in relationship with each of us individually as her children. In what ways has she touched my heart as my mother? In what ways has she brought me healing? In what ways could this relationship be fostered?

4. How can I receive Mary more fully as my loving and tender mother?

5. Why is Mary's role as mother so important in the story of salvation history?

CHAPTER 10
THE VALIANT WOMAN: IMITATING MARY'S ANGELIC KINDNESS AS A STRONG WOMAN

1. How is it that Mary represents the Church as a whole?

2. How does Mary represent the ultimate woman in all of her perfections? What feminine qualities does she purify by example?

3. In what ways can I imitate her kindness, gentleness, and love towards others?

4. In my current state how can I further build up the Church and meet others with greater encouragement and understanding?

5. How does kindness attract others to the truth? Why is it such a powerful disposition for evangelization?

CHAPTER 11

CLOTHED IN THE SON: IMITATING MARY'S HEAVENLY WISDOM AS A BEAUTIFUL WOMAN

1. What makes a woman wise?

2. How do difficulties, trials, and suffering produce character growth when given to Christ?

3. How can I bring a life-giving spirit into the world?

4. What is true beauty in a woman and in what way does it radiate externally?

5. How does Mary relate to all women in all seasons and states? How is it that one Woman could be for all women?

CHAPTER 12

OUR SWEETNESS AND OUR HOPE: IMITATING THE PERFECT WOMAN AS AN IMPERFECT WOMAN

1. In the parable about the little woman, in what ways does she represent all of us?

2. How does her initial disposition reflect lowliness before being exalted? What does this mean in light of my spiritual journey in the ascent to holiness?

3. Why is it significant to begin in the spirit of humility and continually be trained in that disposition throughout my whole life? In what practical ways does this offset my pride?

4. What does it mean to "put on Christ"?

5. Why is it significant that the little woman chose the crown of thorns? In what ways did this draw her closer to the Lord?

6. How is it that I find myself in looking in the eyes of Christ?

7. How am I a "little queen" in light of Mary's queenship?
How am I a "little mother" in light of Mary's motherhood?
How am I a "little daughter" in light of Mary's daughterhood?
How am I a "little bride" in light of Mary's bridal nature?

How to Pray the Holy Rosary

1. Make the Sign of the Cross.

2. Pray the Apostles' Creed (crucifix).

3. Pray an Our Father (first bead).

4. Pray three Hail Marys for faith, hope, and charity (next three beads).

5. Pray the Glory Be and the (optional) Fatima Prayer.

6. Announce the first mystery, and then pray the Our Father. Pray ten Hail Marys on the next "decade" (ten beads), meditating on the mystery. Pray the Glory Be and the (optional) Fatima Prayer.

7. Announce the second mystery, and then pray the Our Father (next single bead). Pray ten Hail Marys on the next "decade" (ten beads), meditating on the mystery. Pray the Glory Be and the (optional) Fatima Prayer.

8. Repeat for each of the remaining mysteries (the remaining beads).

9. After the fifth mystery, pray the Hail, Holy Queen (rosary centerpiece).

10. Conclude with the Rosary prayer.

The Mysteries of the Holy Rosary

Joyful (usually prayed on Mondays and Saturdays)

1. The Annunciation
2. The Visitation
3. The Nativity
4. The Presentation
5. The Finding of Jesus in the Temple

Sorrowful (usually prayed on Tuesdays and Fridays)

1. The Agony in the Garden
2. The Scourging at the Pillar
3. The Crowning with Thorns
4. The Carrying of the Cross
5. The Crucifixion

Glorious (usually prayed on Wednesdays and Sundays)

1. The Resurrection
2. The Ascension
3. The Descent of the Holy Spirit
4. The Assumption of Mary
5. The Coronation of Mary

Luminous (usually prayed on Thursdays)

1. The Baptism of Jesus
2. The Wedding at Cana
3. The Proclamation of the Kingdom
4. The Transfiguration
5. The Institution of the Eucharist

The Prayers of the Rosary

Sign of the Cross

In the name of the Father and of the Son and of the Holy Spirit. Amen.

Apostles' Creed

I believe in God, the Father almighty, Creator of heaven and earth, and in Jesus Christ, his only Son, our Lord, who was conceived by the Holy Spirit, born of the Virgin Mary, suffered under Pontius Pilate, was crucified, died and was buried; he descended to hell; on the third day he rose again from the dead; he ascended into heaven, and is seated at the right hand of God the Father almighty; from there he will come to judge the living and the dead. I believe in the Holy Spirit, the holy catholic Church, the communion of saints, the forgiveness of sins, the resurrection of the body, and life everlasting. Amen.

Our Father

Our Father, who art in heaven, hallowed be thy name; thy kingdom come, thy will be done, on earth as it is in heaven. Give us this day our daily bread, and forgive us our trespasses as we forgive those who trespass against us; and lead us not into temptation, but deliver us from evil. Amen.

Hail Mary

Hail Mary, full of grace, the Lord is with thee. Blessed art thou among women, and blessed is the fruit of thy womb, Jesus. Holy Mary, Mother of God, pray for us sinners, now and at the hour of our death. Amen.

Glory Be

Glory be to the Father, and to the Son, and to the Holy Spirit, as it was in the beginning, is now, and ever shall be, world without end. Amen.

Fatima Prayer

O my Jesus, forgive us our sins, save us from the fires of hell, and lead all souls to heaven, especially those in most need of thy mercy.

Hail, Holy Queen and Rosary Prayer

Hail, Holy Queen, Mother of mercy, our life, our sweetness, and our hope. To thee do we cry, poor banished children of Eve; to thee do we send up our sighs, mourning and weeping in this valley of tears. Turn, then, most gracious advocate, thine eyes of mercy toward us, and after this, our exile, show unto us the blessed fruit of thy womb, Jesus. O clement, O loving, O sweet Virgin Mary.

V. Pray for us, O Holy mother of God.

R. That we may be made worthy of the promises of Christ.

Let us pray. O God, whose only begotten Son, by his life, death, and resurrection, has purchased for us the rewards of eternal life, grant, we beseech thee, that meditating upon these mysteries of the Most Holy Rosary of the Blessed Virgin Mary, we may imitate what they contain and obtain what they promise, through the same Christ our Lord. Amen.

The Prayers of the Rosary in Latin

Signum Crucis (Sign of the Cross)

In nomine Patris et Filii et Spiritus Sancti. Amen.

Symbolum Apostolorum (Apostles' Creed)

Credo in Deum, Patrem Omnipotentem, Creatorem caeli et terræ, et in Jesum Christum, Filium ejus unicum, Dominum nostrum, qui conceptus est de Spiritu Sancto, natus ex Maria Virgine, passus sub Pontio Pilato, crucifíxus, mortuus, et sepultus; descendit ad infernos, tertia die resurrexit a mortuis; ascendit ad caelos, sedet ad dexteram Dei Patris Omnipotentis; inde venturus est judicare vivos et mortuos. Credo in Spiritum Sanctum, sanctam Ecclesiam Catholicam, Sanctorum communionem, remissionem peccatorum, carnis resurrectionem, vitam aeternam. Amen.

Pater Noster (Our Father)

Pater noster, qui es in caelis, sanctificetur nomen tuum. Adveniat regnum tuum. Fiat voluntas tua, sicut in caelo et in terra. Panem nostrum quotidianum da nobis hodie, et dimitte nobis debita nostra, sicut et nos dimittimus debitoribus nostris. Et ne nos inducas in tentationem: sed libera nos a malo. Amen.

Ave Maria (Hail Mary)

Ave Maria, gratia plena, Dominus tecum; benedicta tu in mulieribus, et benedictus fructus ventris tui, Jesus. Sancta Maria, Mater Dei, ora pro nobis peccatoribus, nunc et in hora mortis nostrae. Amen.

Gloria Patri (Glory Be)

Gloria Patri, et Filio, et Spiritui Sancto. Sicut erat in principio et nunc et semper et in saecula sæculorum. Amen.

Oratio Fatima (Fatima Prayer)

O mi Jesu, indulge peccata nostra, conserva nos ab igne inferni, duc omnes ad cæli gloriam, præcipue tua misericordia maxime egentes.

Salve Regina and Rosary Prayer

Salve Regina, Mater Misericordiae: vita, dulcedo, et spes nostra, salve! Ad te clamamus, exsules fílii Hevæ. Ad te suspiramus, gementes et flentes in hac lacrimarum valle. Eja ergo, Advocata nostra, illos tuos misericordes oculos ad nos converte. Et Jesum, benedictum fructum ventris tui, nobis post hoc exsilium ostende. O clemens, O pia, O dulcis Virgo Maria!

V. Ora pro nobis sancta Dei Genitrix

R. Ut digni efficiamur promissionibus Christi.

Oremus: Deus, cujus Unigenitus per vitam, mortem et resurrectionem suam nobis salutis aeternæ praemia comparavit: concede, quaesumus: ut haec mysteria sacratissimo beatae Mariae Virginis Rosario recolentes, et imitemur quod continent, et quod promittunt, assequamur. Per eundem Christum Dominum nostrum.

Acknowledgments

I could not have written this book without the love, support, and true friendship of my dear husband, Joshua Madden, my "theologian" who took the time to read and edit my drafts, check theology, and cheer me on from the moment this idea came and through the entirety of the writing process. Thank you for always believing in me and encouraging me to chase Heaven hand in hand with you. To my children, Felicity, Augustine, Rafqa, Joan, and Colette—and my miscarried babies loved deeply and lost quickly: John, Faustina, Lucy, and Francisco—I am flooded with gratitude at the gift of each of your precious lives. It is a great privilege and my greatest joy to be your mother. I will always be so grateful at the peaceful process in writing and for your excitement when you asked, "Mommy, what are you doing?" and I would say, "I'm writing a book for Mama Mary." To my very dear spiritual director, Fr. Tomasz Szopa, who assured me I would write a book (despite my insistent hesitancy) that would be the fruit of my contemplation. To Ann Driskill, my best friend, my cheerleader, my soul-sister, I am forever grateful for your encouragement and support along every step of this journey. To Claire Dodge, who assured me she would read a book if I wrote it. To Hadleigh Thomas, for reaching out about publishing, to Meredith Wilson, my developmental editor, and to the whole Ascension team who made this possible. It has been a pleasure working with each of you.

Lastly, I would like to thank each of my family members, the Byzantine priests at the International Theological Institute who taught me the mystery and majesty of Our Lady through the Akathist Hymn and deep reverence to her as our warrior-queen-mother. To the Discalced Carmelites in Rochester, New York, who from a young age inspired me in their spirituality and encouraged me to "marry Joshua and never look back," assuring me that holiness is found in the service and love that sprouts from a faithful domestic church.

And finally, to Our Lady under the title of Our Lady of Sorrows, who walked with me through the entire process of writing, who whispered little secrets of her heart, and took my hand into hers as her daughter and led me on as my mother.

I owe you my life.

Notes

1. St. Louis de Montfort, *True Devotion to Mary*, trans. Fr. Frederick Faber, ed. Fathers of the Company of Mary (Rockford, IL: TAN Books and Publishers, 1941), 108.

2. St. Ignatius of Antioch, "The Epistle of Ignatius to the Ephesians," in *The Apostolic Fathers with Justin Martyr and Irenaeus*, ed. Alexander Roberts, James Donaldson, and A. Cleveland Coxe, vol. 1, *The Ante-Nicene Fathers* (Buffalo, NY: Christian Literature Company, 1885), 57.

3. St. John Paul II, general audience address, May 21, 1997.

4. Alice von Hildebrand, *The Privilege of Being a Woman* (Sapientia Press, 2002), title page.